Home Ground

New writing inspired by the Homeless

World Cup in Glasgow

Home Ground

New writing inspired by the Homeless
World Cup in Glasgow

Edited by

Louise Welsh and Zoë Strachan

This selection published in Great Britain in 2017 for Aye Write!
Glasgow's Book Festival by Glasgow Libraries
The Mitchell Library, 201 North Street, Glasgow G37DN
Tel: 01412872999 · www.glasgowlife.org.uk/libraries

A CIP catalogue record for this book is available from the British Library.

ISBN: 978-0-906169-72-8
eISBN: 978-0-906169-73-5

Printed by **Bell and Bain Ltd** – www.bell-bain.com

Contents

Preface

When George Square was transformed to host the 2016 Homeless World Cup there was an expectation that once again Glasgow would deliver a truly great event.

We did.

For seven days it became "the most inspiring place on the planet" as teams came together from across the world to celebrate and highlight the year round life-changing work being done by the Homeless World Cup National Partner network.

The event also aimed to raise awareness of homelessness and to provide a means for homeless people to change their lives through the power of football.

Glasgow is a natural venue for this event. We are not only a city with a global reputation for delivering events; we have also gained world-wide fame for the warmth of the welcome visitors get and for our inclusivity.

After all, "People Make Glasgow".

More than five hundred players arrived in the heart of the city in the summer of 2016, each with their own story to tell; each on a journey to create a better life for themselves.

The success of the Homeless World Cup can be measured, in part, through the 80,000 spectators who came to watch the sixty-four competing teams from fifty-one nations but it should also be viewed as a highly visible moment amid years of work.

This book is a more permanent legacy of those days in the summer of 2016 and it will be shared, at no cost, throughout Glasgow during Aye Write! Glasgow's Book Festival and with an e-publication available to download online.

It is a collection of new writing, all of it covering themes of place, space, identity and homelessness, much of it by new writers and all of it with something to say about the experience of issues related to homelessness.

It is a collection of extraordinary power and great relevance and it brings with it many strong and often conflicting emotions.

It is a book that is unflinching in the way that it tackles its subject matter and sometimes the writer has direct experience of homelessness.

We are grateful to the writers who took their first steps with us before the Homeless World Cup and who have contributed to something that is truly special and unique.

Our profound thanks are also due to Louise Welsh and Zoë Strachan who have edited this book and shaped this outstanding collection.

Their unstinting generosity, skill, encouragement and willingness to help, brought this book to life.

Many of those who took part were mentored throughout their writing and we are grateful to all who gave their time, talent and advice to support this work. Thanks to tutors from University of Strathclyde's Centre for Lifelong Learning and mentors from University of Glasgow's MLitt Creative Writing course.

This book has been published by Glasgow Libraries with the support of Freight Design who have brought enormous enthusiasm and their award winning expertise and provided guidance throughout.

Home Ground was an idea to build a legacy of the Homeless World Cup. It has been supported through the Big Lottery Fund.

That these stories are in print is thanks to all these supporters and many, many more.

Our hope is that beyond those inspiring days of July 2016, Home Ground can serve as a further reminder of some of the wonderful work being done around the world to help homeless people.

If we all do something, whether big or small, we can work to eradicating homelessness both at home and around the world. The Homeless World Cup is an inspiration, it shows what can be achieved through the power of sport. This book is testament to its success.

Councillor Archie Graham OBE
Chair, Glasgow Life
Depute Leader, Glasgow City Council

What a Team!

Zoë Strachan

The Public Library Act was extended to Scotland in 1853. Those who campaigned for free public libraries thought that reading was morally uplifting, and that it might keep the lower classes out of the pub. The main argument against libraries was that they would educate the lower orders and so foment social and political agitation. It's no accident that libraries are amongst the first of our services to be threatened when cuts are made to public spending. When people can read, and have free access to books, they're more likely to see their world clearly, and question things about it. The work included in this anthology is amazing in many ways, not least of which is that it holds that power to make us think about things differently, and imagine how our lives might change.

The best thing about reading is that it's fun, but it is also true that books are good for us, whether they are morally uplifting or not. Sometimes the people we read about are real, and sometimes they are fictional creations. It doesn't matter. In learning about them, about how they think and see the world, by walking in their shoes for the length of a story or novel, we develop empathy. We expand our understanding. And when we come to write stories or poems of our own, we communicate our thoughts and feelings with others. We choose our words, shape our sentences, give voice to our ideas. In doing so, we hope that we'll pass the ball of understanding to someone else, and that they'll run with it for a while before passing it on in turn.

Many of the pieces in this anthology tackle homelessness as a theme, but homelessness is never the whole story. Instead these pieces are about individual people in their own unique circumstances, and all the joys, tragedies and hopes that propel their lives. It is a collection grounded in Glasgow, although many stories take us further afield, to Paris and Orkney and Southern Sudan. Streets that are familiar as old friends appear here in new guises, as the site of a new life, or of neglect and death, or of raucous fun, or of the memories that make us who we are. Our city has many facets. As do the buildings we live in, if we're lucky enough to have a roof over our heads. Houses here are sometimes safe and warm, and sometimes full of risk. Some characters are chancing everything for their hopes and dreams, others are confronting the demons that lurk inside us and inside our families. Home ground emerges as a complicated idea. Even the manicured pitch of a professional football field may not be as solid as it looks.

Reading through the submissions for the anthology was thrilling. We didn't know what to expect, and each piece was different and surprising. There are some astonishingly moving pieces here; writing that is honest, brave and remarkable in its clear-sightedness. There are stories that had us in stitches through the vividness of the characters' voices and the sheer absurd hilarity of their observations. The tone ranges from riotous to pensive to positively sinister. We think that it is a really good collection: far-ranging, entertaining and thought-provoking.

The Homeless World Cup uses football to counter the isolation of homelessness, and its detrimental effect on the ability to share, communicate thoughts, and work with others. The writers involved in this anthology have proved that they can communicate their thoughts brilliantly, and that they can work with each other as learners, mentors or simply people engaged in the shared endeavour of crafting poems and stories. Nobody is sitting on the side-lines; this is a winning team.

Some names may be familiar to avid readers (not to mention football fans). We have award-winning, bestselling authors in the line-up. Alongside them there are striking new talents, some donning their literary shirts for the very first time. Deliberately, we haven't included any biographies, so it's up to you to guess who is established and who is new. On these pages at least, it's a level playing field.

Books can change the world, but we're not asking quite so much of this one. Instead, we hope it will take you to places that you recognise and places that you've never been. The title says it all: Home Ground. It's a chance to celebrate and think about the city we live in and the things we share as human beings. And if along the way it makes you laugh or brings a tear to your eye, so much the better.

Enjoy!

Homeless: Sleeping Rough, Living Rough, Being Invisible

Louise Welsh

Walk through the centre of Glasgow – the centre of any city – late at night or early in the morning and you will see homeless people. City-dwellers are not devoid of empathy, but we can turn on selective vision. We head for home, the pub, a restaurant, deleting rough sleepers from our vision, as easily as we shift our camera lens to erase an ugly building from an otherwise picturesque view.

You don't have to be on the streets to be invisible. Homeless people occupy our workplaces, the shops we visit and the factories that supply them. They sit beside us on the bus, study in our schools and colleges. They even might be processing your application for accommodation, praying that they too can find a place to call home.

This winter national newspapers reported that some employees of Amazon UK's Dunfermline depot were camping in woodland close to the warehouse in sub-zero temperatures. These workers were desperate to keep their jobs, but their wages were so low, they could not afford travel costs to and from their homes.[1]

Daisy May Hudson was in her early twenties and studying drama when her family's landlord decided to sell the house they had rented for thirteen years. She attempted to banish some of her feelings of powerlessness by filming their experience of homelessness. The result is in her debut documentary *HalfWay*. 'We'd always considered ourselves 'a normal family', then suddenly we had to get our heads around the fact that we were homeless, and it came as a big shock'.[2] Hudson's sister, who was thirteen at the time and studying for exams, kept the

[1] *The Independent*, 'Hard-pressed Amazon workers in Scotland sleeping in tents near warehouse to save money' (Saturday 10th December 2016) http://www.independent.co.uk/news/uk/home-news/amazon-workers-sleep-tents-dunfermline-fife-scotland-a7467657.html

[2] *The Guardian* 'Daisy-May Hudson: 'Being homeless came as a big shock' (Wednesday 11th November 2015) https://www.theguardian.com/society/2015/nov/11/homeless-shock-daisy-may-hudson-film-half-way.

family's situation a secret from her friends.

It is not simply embarrassment or misplaced shame that makes people conceal their homelessness from friends and colleagues, though these emotions are very real. Being homeless also has a profound impact on employability.

Aileen Matthews, an employee of Homes for Haringey, struggled to pay rent of £1,200 a month to her private landlord. When she fell into arrears in the winter of 2016 and was evicted, she and her teenage son Kishur sought temporary shelter in a garage. They searched for a new flat to rent but were repeatedly told that landlords, 'only wanted tenants who were earning at least £30,000.' Aileen went to the council and declared herself and her son homeless. 'I was made to feel so worthless by the member of staff who dealt with me. She forced me to tell her where we were sleeping. A couple of days later I was called in to see my manager and was told I was being suspended because I was sleeping in a council estate garage.'[3] Homes for Haringey's mission statement is, 'We want to prevent homelessness whenever possible.'

The Homeless World Cup recognises that homelessness is a global issue. It brings together people of different ethnicities and religions from across the globe to share the beautiful game and so much more. It is especially pleasing that Glasgow, with its history of football and religious rivalry, should have hosted this celebration of inclusivity in sport. Perhaps you know only too well how it feels to be homeless; perhaps you fear that you will experience it in the future. The factors that cause homelessness will not be resolved by games of football or even by this anthology, but sport and stories help us to hear the voices of others. We see each other. We see ourselves.

This anthology is a kaleidoscope of voices, styles, concerns and subject matters. It is as varied as the individuals who have contributed to it. Some of them have experienced homelessness, others have not. They share a love of life, a love of words. None of them is invisible.

[3] *The Guardian* 'Homelessness group worker suspended for sleeping rough in council garage' (22nd December 2016) https://www.theguardian.com/uk-news/2016/dec/22/woman-working-for-homelessness-group-suspended-for-sleeping-rough

From Happiness to Homelessness: One Man's Journey to Hell and Back

David Farrell

Celtic Park, October 1993. It's 1:1 and the Scottish League Cup Final hangs in the balance. Ten minutes to go and it's close. So close we can almost reach out and feel the cold, silver handle of the trophy. No one ever tells you that, how cold the handles are in your hands. I've toiled and sacrificed all of my twenty-three years and 361 days for this. Never in my wildest dreams did I think I'd be here, on the cusp of possibly winning a national cup final. It was everything I and many of my contemporaries from Dennistoun had aspired to, as we played out our very own Cup Finals, night after night in the playgrounds of St. Denis Primary and Whitehill secondary schools. Those were our Hampden (although on this occasion the Cup Final was played in the east end of Glasgow due to the refurbishment of the national stadium; a mishmash of a project resulting in the unfit carbuncle we now have sitting on the south side). We'd batter into each other on the solid concrete and barge our pals into the unforgiving green school railings, all in the pursuit of getting *there*. Eight, ten then and sometimes even twelve and fourteen-a-side on a Sunday. For a game on that scale, we had to move up to 'the cricky', an old cricket pitch, now a red ash, full sized football ground that doubled as Whitehill school playing fields. On those particular Sundays, we had to wait our turn to grace the hallowed, unforgiving red blaes as the older guys and grown men played out their very own, laboured fantasies before succumbing to a very obvious lack of both fitness and finesse and heading to the pub for a few pints, Scotsport and then Sunday dinner at whatever time they limped home.

There was where I was now, standing on the six yard line at Celtic Park, helpless as the ball bounces two agonising yards in front of me and up, over my head. As I turn, we're in a good position, defenders goal side and the only Rangers player in the frame, Ally McCoist, has his back to goal and is surrounded by Hibernian green and white. In a flash, he chests the ball upward before flicking, with his back still to goal, an overhead bicycle kick into the bottom corner of the net to send the blue legions into unbridled rapture. We huffed and puffed through those final few minutes, but in truth it was never to be our day. McCoist had been out injured for five months after breaking his leg for Scotland, and he was destined to score that sickening, spectacular winner on his comeback.

At that moment, everything feels very alone. You're surrounded by team mates yet lost in splendid isolation. Half of the 50,000 crowd are screaming in ecstasy while the other half just want to wave goodbye to their team and then trudge disconsolate from the ground. As players, you want to see your family and go over to your fans to show them your appreciation. A wave, a false smile and that pitiful 'thank you' clap that all players do at the end of a game. We never even got to do that as the manager ushered us off the pitch after watching Rangers get their hands on the glorious, cold handles of the League Cup. Apparently he wasn't allowing us to celebrate being beaten. A harsh lesson indeed. I managed to catch my partner's eye as we were trudging off and then my Dad, brother and sister. You do everything to avoid looking at the other end and the opposing throng. Their celebrations and over exuberant cheering and waving make for a nauseous visual cocktail. But I couldn't help it. As I skimmed seamlessly over the thousands of celebrating Rangers fans, I caught a glimpse of Robert, a lad from Dennistoun who had been among the group who would regularly go hammer and tongs on 'the cricky'. He had been a decent player, one of many from the East End who had eventually managed to turn professional, although his journey into the game at the top level turned out to be much more fleeting than mine had.

Brief spells in the lower leagues were to be his only shot at getting *there*. We had been rivals, really, Robert went to the Protestant school and I the Catholic one. That's the way it was in Dennistoun. You were either one or the other, Celtic or Rangers, Green or Blue, Tim or Hun, Fenian or Orange. All pals and no one EVER got offended. We all played football together, mixing and changing the teams every night, before battering into tackles without a thought for either's safety or wellbeing. It was a wonderful way to grow up. All we ever wanted do was win and here was Robert, knee deep in my misery, yet celebrating like HE had just won the cup. He wasn't paying any attention to me of course, he was much more interested in trying to catch the eye of Golden Bollocks McCoist and the rest of his Rangers idols as they made their way up the stairs to get their sweaty palms on the trophy. I turned away as I couldn't bear the sight of him lifting it high above his head to the adulation of his people (and Robert). And with that, he was gone, lost among the celebrating blue legions now drifting from sight and making their way towards exits and sweet tasting victory drams. As I made my way down the tunnel and into the changing room, Robert was by now a distant memory and I was left to wallow in my devastation at having got *there* and not got my hands cold.

It was a long time before I seen him again. We'd occasionally cross paths in the nightclubs of Glasgow, where he'd regale me with stories of how he was better than me and how he should have 'made it'. This was a common theme in Glasgow as there was a never-ending stream of dreamers and delusionists, all too eager to tell you how good they were, or that they were much better than me and that THEY should have been the ones getting free entry to the dancin'. It was water off a duck's back of course; I couldn't care less what they thought, which may seem a very ungracious attitude, but I'd worked extremely hard to be a footballer and made huge sacrifices. I deserved to be the one skipping the queue on a Saturday night.

We were no longer close, but it was always good to see Robert alongside the stilettos and handbags of Glasgow's dance floors. He was outgoing, smart, always well dressed and, unlike me, he loved a sunbed. You could see him coming from a mile off as he smiled, rather than shimmied his way across to the bar, to fire yet another jibe or light hearted quip my way. The sunbed was the status symbol of the Glasgow 'in crowd', although personally I much preferred Tenerife to Tanerife. And yet, through all the bravado and fake tan and a smile that would have lit up George Square, I always felt Robert was guarded, never quite telling me the full story. I was sure he was keeping things to himself. There was a facade there that I could never quite break down, but I never seen him often enough or was even remotely bothered enough to probe or want to get beneath the surface and find out why. Well, it wasn't my problem was it?

We had been very similar. Both good at football, both brought up in the east end and both desperate to make it. Like most of us, I drifted through my adult years and lost contact with so many people. I hadn't seen my old pal for quite some time until incredibly, whilst watching the Scottish news, it was seeing Robert lift a football trophy of all things, that was to be the catalyst to finding out so much more about HIS 'drifting' years.

Circumstances, hard work and a little bit of luck meant that I had managed an eighteen year playing career whilst Robert had stumbled his way through little more than eighteen months. However, in Paris 2011, Robert found his *there.*

I was reading the sports pages of the following day's Daily Record before it really sunk in. I'd glossed over the news bulletin the previous evening where a ragamuffin bunch of 16–40s were celebrating something. They all wore the full Scotland replica kit and were doing that team photo thing we've all seen a million times before where pitchside, the captain holds the trophy aloft in the midst of his celebrating team mates, just as McCoist had done all those years ago. Only this time, there was a familiar face, slap bang in the middle, getting his hands cold. I'd recognise that smile anywhere. Robert was celebrating ON the pitch as, remarkably, a Scotland team had won a football tournament. A little more purposeful reading beyond staring aghast at the original picture revealed we had won the Homeless World Cup. I didn't even know it was a 'thing'. A World Cup, for the homeless?

Growing up in Dennistoun I wasn't even aware of homelessness other than it was something you occasionally came across on American TV shows like *Starsky and Hutch* and *Hill Street Blues.* We were hardly living in a leafy suburb and there were less silver spoons there than in a Blackpool B&B, but I never knew anyone who was sleeping rough. The bad guys would disappear from sight, under the bridges and waterways of Brooklyn, the Bronx and Manhattan. Charging through a sea of cardboard boxes and sleeping bags to avoid arrest, before looking back to make sure they hadn't disturbed anyone from their stupor. That was my perception growing up, that it was a problem on the other side of the world, not on my own doorstep. But this time it wasn't an eighties cop show and Robert was from the hood, surely he couldn't have been homeless, could he?

Football can be a cruel game. Not many can be as lucky as I was and manage to survive playing for eighteen years and coaching for another twelve. It continuously knocks you down and stamps all over you through the never-ending cycle of free transfers, backstabbing and one year contracts. Most of it is a far cry from what you see happening now with satellite TV's millions dwarfing the game. For most of us, the journeymen, it was just another way to earn a living and just as powerful a drug as any you can buy on street corners. It's a little known fact that on leaving football, the incidence of depression and divorce is much higher than in many other mainstream professions. It's that drug I was talking about and the addiction to it. When football tosses you on to the scrapheap, like a sweaty sock on the dressing room floor, you are forced to find a REAL job and nothing replaces the feeling of fulfilment and excitement. Robert, unbeknownst to me, had indirectly been a victim of that. Those inner mental demons, that I had vaguely suspected, had affected him in a cruel, devastating way and only his tough school playground upbringing would bring him back from the abyss of depression.

His brief sojourn into professional football was never going to be enough to satisfy that craving honed on the streets of the East End. A couple of years in the game serves only to take the edge off the addiction and whilst he rebuilt his life with all the vigour and verve expected of 'one of the boys', the rejection never goes away. His resolve and desire to build a career with his family ensured he found a good job and a wife and kids to be proud of, but on the back of a harsh recession, redundancy was to be the final nail in a coffin which had already been lowered to the point of no return on various occasions. Depression set in and started a downward spiral which was ultimately to lead to a marital split, moving out of the family home, losing access to the kids and the ignominy of an extended family unit who no longer wanted anything to do with him.

I have to confess that back then, I had common misconceptions about homelessness. They were all addicts, alcoholics and vagrants, right? There was no way someone like Robert, or even God forbid, someone like me, could possibly have fallen into that unedifying lifestyle, was there? Well Robert's story is the proof that mine, and many other people's prejudiced ideas, couldn't be further from reality. For many, it's not a choice or a decision that has been taken to be *there*. Who in their right mind would ever choose to be homeless? Not me, not you and not Robert. On the back of losing that job, he ended up sleeping rough. Moving from hostel to hostel and occasionally spending the odd evening at Her Majesty's pleasure. How he ever found the strength to lift that trophy in Paris I'll never know. But lift it he did.

Incredibly, he had found support in the form of one of the things that had brought him to his knees: football. A team from Scotland, pulled together by an amazing group of people who'd managed to replicate the camaraderie, spirit and sense of belonging to something that would put many professional football clubs to shame, gave him, and many others, their life back. Not only that, he got his kids back, his family back, but most importantly, his self-esteem back. When I bumped into him again this year at of all places, the wonderful spectacle that was Glasgow hosting the Homeless World Cup, he also had his swagger back. Selflessly, he was now coaching the team that had given him his inspiration and a sense of worth at his lowest ebb. Harnessing that community spirit and spreading it among the latest group of waifs and strays sleeping on the streets of Glasgow. Lawyers, junkies, teachers, drunks, doctors, asylum seekers and ex-footballers all on the same team, treading the same well-worn path. Fighting to stay alive every night in the same way Robert did.

That the United Kingdom, with an annual defence budget alone of £35 BILLION, should have so many thousands of homeless people sleeping rough on our streets, night after night, is shameful. That some of those billions cannot be directed at shelters and housing, to allow those a little less fortunate to keep safe and dry at night, should make our policy makers cower with embarrassment. That the homeless should have to rely on charity, foodbanks, handouts and soup kitchens for any hope of a hot meal on a daily basis and live such a hand to mouth existence, day after day, is something that every one of us should have on our conscience. Sure, there are many who have not helped themselves, whether that be addiction, alcoholism, crime or bad choices that has driven them to a life of cardboard boxes and mouldy sleeping bags. However, Robert and many, many others have been no more than a victim of circumstance and neither should be forced into losing not only their worldly possessions, but also their dignity. Robert's story should serve us well to remember that none of us is ever a million miles away from being homeless. In these worrying times of financial hardship and uncertainty, many families are only one pay away from poverty. The reality of homelessness is not just a Starsky and Hutch fantasy, it's happening right here on our doorstep. Luckily, Robert was able to fight and scratch his way out from the depths of despair. Many others, for one reason or another will NEVER get out and will remain homeless for the rest of their lives. Think about that the next time you cross the street to avoid the crumpled heap on the pavement. Their story, like Robert's, may not be all it seems.

Home Ground

James Ramsay

Why did I ever want to get older when I was young? It's actually quite ironic now that I`m older, I want to be younger.

It's a messed up situation.

I remember sitting in the dentist chair, with my hands tightly gripped to the chair. As soon as I seen the needle that he was going to put in my mouth, I tried to punch him! I hated needles, even the sight of one would make me feel sick. I remember a time when I was in school and we were getting our BCG jags, I got to the front of the queue and just walked away, that's how scared I was.

Now I put needles in myself all the time, sometimes I even enjoy it... It`s FUCKED UP I KNOW!

I became a heroin addict at the age of seventeen. I'm now forty-nine, and I`ve lost most of the important things in my life. I also contracted hepatitis C.

When I was eight years old I moved from a tenement house in inner city Glasgow, where the toilet was in the back, close to a place called Summerston. It was a new housing scheme outside Glasgow, I always remember the toilets and the closes in the tenements were always very clean, there would always be some neighbour out with her head scarf on, washing the toilet and the close. In the toilet on the bottom landing of where I lived, there was a big green wrought iron ringer, and my sister would always get me to put my fingers in the wheels to try and catch them.

The house that we moved to in Summerston not only had a toilet with a bath upstairs, but there was also a small toilet downstairs, so it was like moving into a mansion with countryside and building work all around me. It was a fantasy world for an eight-year-old boy and I loved it so much.

I was so unused to the countryside that I used to think corn was just long grass. Anyway, my friends and I started egg collecting as it was an adventure. I remember we found an egg and we would pierce a pin hole on the egg, one on the top and one on the bottom, that way you could just blow at one end of the egg and the yolk would come out of the bottom.

One day I tried it, and the egg burst open and there in front of me was a young dead chick. I felt so bad about this, I cried like a baby… I think I cried all day and felt so guilty about it, so from then on in, I did what I could do to make sure that the egg wasn`t ready to hatch. I would do this by holding the egg in my hands and making sure that the egg wasn`t too warm nor heavy. I would also hold it up to the sunlight, so I made sure I followed all these rules before I blew an egg again.

There was lots of building work going on around us. We used to do dares to see who would jump out of the highest buildings onto the piles of sand that was there for the building work, I was always the most daring, and would always jump from the highest landing or building!

There was one time that we tried to build a diving board down at the River Kelvin, as we used to swim there during the summertime. So we got the biggest plank that we could find, and carried it down to the place where we used to swim in the river.

We just thought if we dug a deep hole and placed the plank in, that it should work, but every time we tried it, it just fell apart. I came up with an idea… what I done was moved the hole and the plank along the sandy bank just a little bit. I got the guys to look for the biggest boulders that they could find and I dug a shallow hole. I held the plank in and got the guys to wrestle the boulder on top of the plank, so that it was a tight fit… and honestly… I mean it… That diving dale worked just like a dream, I was so proud of myself that I bragged about it for years… Ha-ha!! And I still do!!

My life went on like this for a while, looking for birds' nests. Swimming in the river and making swings from the tallest trees that we could climb. It was a great time and place for a young boy, but before long the darkness slowly crept in. What happened to all my friends, why can`t I ring them up, just to say hello, or ask them to go for a game of pool and a pint? I couldn`t as they were all dead, dead from catching HIV, I was just fortunate that I did not catch it. Sometimes I ask myself, why am I still here? Maybe it was only to have my two beautiful children, but now I feel there is no-one for me, as my children are no longer kids, they have flown their nest and emigrated to another country.

I started skipping school and hanging around with the wrong kinds of people. There was a family who lived across the street from me, and they were all really mixed up with crime and the rough side of life. Anyway, the older brother had just been released from prison, and he started selling heroin. Drugs were all kind of new back then around 1984. Gerry asked me if I would sell drugs for him. I just thought that it would be another adventure. I never really had a clue of what I was letting myself in for.

These days all the young boys know the dangers of taking drugs and becoming an addict, but back then we had nothing to aspire to and no way of knowing the dangers of taking heroin. I became an addict, a 'junky' and it wasn't only me. All my friends started using heroin too, it was like 'the new trend'.

Before long Gerry stopped giving me heroin to sell as I was using so much of it myself that I couldn't pay him. Gerry had a young brother called Tommy, and sometimes he would steal bits of heroin off his brother to sell to me and my friends at a knocked off price. Before long he became a drug addict himself. My friends and I were never really bad guys, we were just stupid, young and vulnerable. Drugs took everything away. It took my family, my friends, my confidence, my self-esteem. It also made me lose a lot of years in my life that I can never get back.

Life went on like this for years, crime, drugs, prisons and homelessness. Don't get me wrong, at times it could be very exciting, but mostly the times were just bad.

In 1990 I was given the chance to go to a rehabilitation centre in Sheffield. It took me some time to settle in, as by this time I had a beautiful eighteen month young daughter who I loved very much.

One day they asked us to write down about a really bad time or experience in our lives. By this time I was only twenty-three years old, and a lot of things happened to me since using heroin but there was one event that really changed my life forever.

I was eighteen in April 1986 and by this time Gerry was in prison yet again, but his youngest brother Tommy was still using drugs. I will always remember it was a Saturday night and about four of us went to buy drugs from a guy in the flats nearby from where we lived, but by the time we got there, the dealer had sold out. So we decided to go to Possilpark. This was always a bit dangerous as by this time drugs had become right rife in Possil, so there was always the chance of being ripped off at knife point or being sold shit stuff. But by luck or bad luck, depending on which way you look at it, we met someone who seemed ok. He told us that the heroin he had was strong and had just came from down London.

Tommy, another friend of ours, and I ended up going back to my parents' house as they were out at a wedding. We had all bought three £5 bags of heroin. I decided just to take one, as the guy told us that the stuff was strong. I told Tommy not to take any more, but instead, he decided to take two £5 bags. He asked me to help him find a vein as his body was that bad. I remember trying to inject him, but in the end I was so wasted that I don't know if I did help him to find a vein or if he got it by himself. I then started to tidy my room and I decided to look over at Tommy, while my other friend was finishing off his hit. Tommy was lying on my bed, his skin was blue and his lips were grey. I started to freak out as I knew my parents would be home soon. Somehow my other friend and I managed to wrestle him outside as he was a dead weight. We got him to a nearby bench and laid him down on it. You must understand I was only eighteen and I had never experienced someone take an overdose in front of me.

I phoned an ambulance that seemed to take forever to come, I didn't even know about the recovery position or resuscitation techniques, so I just tried to keep him awake. Now and then he would make gurgling noises which made me think that he was ok. When the ambulance finally arrived, I felt so relieved. I told the paramedics what Tommy had taken. I gave them my name and address. I just thought that Tommy would be ok, as I had heard of people taking overdoses in the past and being taken to hospital, where they would be released that day. I knew that Tommy still had a fiver bag in his pocket, but I just thought that it would be ok to leave it.

The next morning I woke up and thought, as soon as I was ready, I would go and find out how Tommy was. Before long, there was a chap at my front door. It was Tommy's other brother Davie, who is also another bit of a head-case. Davie asked me to come out as he wanted to talk to me. The first thing I asked him was, how's Tommy keeping? He told me Tommy was dead.

I refused to believe him, but I soon realised it was true as he pulled out a massive knife and tried to attack me. I managed to run away, and stayed away, but by the end of the day I had been found and charged with culpable homicide. I remember the words the police said to me...

'You James Ramsay, did wilfully and culpably kill the said Thomas Rae!'

I felt so deflated, as if my whole world was falling apart.

The next day I was released from the Glasgow Sheriff Court on bail, things started to become really fucked up after that. I became a target and so did my family. Before long Gerry was back out of prison, he was the real dangerous one. I tried my best to stay at home, but realised I needed to get away to protect my family, as my Mum's dog was found dead in a nearby Park with two crossbow bolts through his body, it was so sad. The guilt was just becoming worse and worse for me.

At this time I knew a girl called Denise who had a house of her own, and I knew that she would allow me to stay there until I could find somewhere else to stay.

Before long the court case came up, it was quite a big thing back then in 1987 as this was a first case of this kind in Scotland. It turned out that the fiver bag of heroin that I left in Tommy's pocket had been tested by forensics and the heroin was very near pure, it was 92%. My lawyer called the drug squad up to the witness stand and they explained the strongest percent of heroin on the streets back then was between 15 and 25% max. So in actual fact, my lawyer explained that my friends and I went out to score and it was very unfortunate that this time the gear was of such a high percentage. With the help of my QC Gordon Jackson, I was found not guilty. I was so relieved, but yet I still felt under threat by Tommy's family.

My friend Denise was still allowing me to stay at hers. Our friendship became more than that, it became a relationship and I stayed with her for thirty years and we had two beautiful children together, although we are now apart.

Anyway, the court case was over with but I still felt like a hunted animal. I had been shot at twice, and felt threat wherever I went, it was very stressful, it was like a game of cat and mouse.

So in a way, my life was still all over the place… still using heroin, being thrown out by Denise and being homeless for weeks and months at a time.

It's mysterious how life actually works as even although Tommy's death was such a tragedy, ironically it saved my life. During this period of time, my other friends were all using a girl's house as a shooting up den. It so happened her sister was a prostitute living out in Edinburgh, and in this time in 1987 HIV was rife in Edinburgh. It wasn't long before the shared needles and the unprotected sex got them all infected with AIDS. My life was spared as I wasn't around at this time, I was still moving around having to watch my back. If it hadn't been for this, I would have done what my friends were doing and I would have contracted the virus too. Tommy's death saved my life.

All of Tommy's brothers died one by one with a heroin overdose. One of the brothers was found dead in his car and my sister was a police officer at the time, and she was at his autopsy. It's funny how life works out eh?

Sometimes I still feel lost, and I still feel as though I am running, but life is getting better for me.

The Gift of Friendship

Jacqui Cathcart

We go through life with very few people
I mean the real people not just pretend
Come across a lot of acquaintances too
But only a few really will be true.

Who is your real friend, how do you know?
How can you tell, how does it show
Let me tell you what friendship is all about
It's trusting each other without a doubt.

It's doing for them what they'd do for you
Your darkest days they'll help you through
When you really need them, they'll be there
Showing just how much for you they care.

Friends never want repaid for what they do
Will try to understand just because it's you
Not because they have to do these things
Because they want to, that's what friendship brings.

The time or place doesn't matter at all
No problem's too big for them or too small
Friends will help each other in every way
What the time is, night or day.

Friends accept our faults for what they are
Cos the good points outweigh the bad by far
Comfort you when you're feeling low or sad
Sharing the good times as well as the bad.

With true friendship there's a strong bond
You'll just know the difference and won't be conned
Some people will try their best to pretend
For their own purposes to be your friend.

Real friends really are few and far between
So don't lose touch with them once you've seen
They're truly for real and sure they care too
Sharing that special something only real friends do.

Yellow House

Peter McCune

The ghost came at three in the morning. I was in bed, completely awake, when the door creaked open. I recognised him straight away, so I didn't even have time to think it was a burglar and shite myself. Even though he'd been dead for eight years, the man in front of me was clearly my dad – which I suppose should've been scarier than a burglar, but it wasn't.

'Mark me,' he said, his voice thick and slurred.

'What?' I said.

'Revenge my foul and most unnatural murder,' he said, and this time it was obvious he was drunk.

'Dad? You're quoting Hamlet at me? That's ridiculous!'

He swayed a little on the spot and had to hold on to the chest of drawers to steady himself. I crawled down my bed to get a better look at him. Up a little closer, in the almost dark, I could see his skin was a deep mustard yellow. I had to reach back and turn on my bedside lamp to get a better look at him. If I was the kind of guy who screamed, then I think I would have screamed my head off. His skin was brighter, more like Simpson's skin, and the whites of his eyes were a sort of neon yellow, like sulphur. I could smell him too, and he smelled like he always had: cheap wine, stale smoke, and body odour.

'Dad?' I said to him. 'You're pissed. You're actually pissed. How the hell can a ghost get drunk?'

'I don't know what's happened. I don't know why they did it, but they poured poison in my ear.'

'No, Dad, they didn't do anything. You poisoned yourself.'

'Yes,' he said, his eyes wet with tears. 'In the porches of my ear he did pour this leprous distilment—'

'—Jesus, Dad! Will you stop quoting that fucking play.'

Nobody could ever make me angry like my dad.

'Mark me!' he said again, then he jerked forward and started boaking on the carpet.

'No, Dad, I'm not gonna fucking *mark you*,' I said. I had no idea what he even meant by that.

I went out to get him a glass of water and I expected the room to be empty when I got back. I was so angry I think I wanted him to be gone. But he was still there, and at least he'd stopped being sick.

I gave him the glass and he thanked me, then he sipped at the water without saying a word. He was just staring at the wall, almost a statue, almost catatonic. I got a better look at him, then, because I was standing above him. He looked worse than I'd ever seen him. His wispy beard had grown out and he'd lost so much weight that his cheeks and eyes had sunken in, showing the outline of his skull. But he wasn't yellow when I saw him last. Jesus, if he'd been jaundiced I would've called an ambulance right away.

I sat down beside him and I couldn't think of anything to say. Eight years since I'd seen him and I struggled to think of a single talking point. So we sat in silence, and it was the sort of silence that gets stronger and harder to break the longer you're in it. The only sounds were the ticking clock from the next room and Dad's laboured breaths. I wondered why a ghost should breathe at all. Then I got an idea that this was my one chance to talk to him and that I had to forget how impossible all of this was so that I could maybe say something worthwhile to him.

'I sometimes feel like you're haunting me through my body,' I said.

Dad turned to face me, his face scrunched up into a question.

'Yeah,' I continued. 'I look the most like you out of the three of us – especially with these skinny little goat legs I've got. And there's this stupid high-pitched laugh I do sometimes and it's just like the way you used to laugh. I only started doing it after you died. And sometimes it feels like I look so much like you that I am you, wearing your skin over mine, moving your mouth to say my words. And when I get that feeling it's like I've come home to that yellow house, like I'm with you again.'

'I think I understand,' he said, after a while. 'I felt that way with my father. Like I inherited his body when he died.'

'Yes,' I said, and I probably sounded happier than I should have, but it was a weird thing to admit to anyone, let alone him, so I was just relieved that he got it.

'Have you been back to the house?' he asked me.

'No,' I said. 'Not really. I just drove past it a few times.' And maybe it was because he was there with me, but I could see that strange little yellow house so clearly at that moment.

'D'you remember the time you were passed out, stone drunk,' I said, 'so I put a whole teaspoon of mustard in your mouth to teach you a lesson?'

He laughed when I said that. It was that same little goofy laugh. Our laugh.

'Yeah,' he said, 'you little bugger. And it was English mustard, too. The big guns. I thought I was dying.'

I was laughing too, and it was so nice and normal that I forgot how weird the whole thing was.

'You screamed and rubbed your tongue on the carpet. Robby and Jane were laughing so much they couldn't breathe, but I was scared I'd get in trouble.'

'I was probably just too drunk to punish you,' he said, when he finally stopped laughing.

'Yeah. Probably. D'you remember that time Jane poured a jug of water over your head because you'd passed out in the middle of the floor?'

'No. I don't,' he said. 'But I'll take your word for it.'

'Yeah. It was hilarious.'

'Do you have any nice stories about me?' he asked.

'Yeah,' I said. 'Of course I do. I still tell people about that time you made the Olympic Games for all of the kids in the street. D'you remember that?'

He frowned, and I could almost hear his brain trying to find the memory. 'No,' he said, 'I don't remember that either. I've forgotten more than I remember, I guess. The drink'll do that to you.'

'That's okay. I'll tell you about it. I think Jane and I were maybe eight, and Robby was ten. We were playing with the other kids in the street – about six or seven of them – and you came out and asked if we wanted to do the Olympics.'

'Yeah?' he smiled and there was something childish about it. 'Sounds fun.'

'It was. You made up a bunch of wee games where we had to do things like see who could throw the most stones into flower pots and who could walk in the straightest line after they'd been blindfolded and spun around a bunch of times. Stuff like that. Everyone said you were the most fun dad and I remember how I couldn't stop smiling because you were my dad and they all wished you were theirs.'

Dad started crying then, his shoulders chugging up and down, and he sobbed every now and then, but he was mostly silent. I think it was that special kind of pain where you can't even make a noise or you might never stop.

'I'm sorry I didn't cry when I heard you'd died,' I said, because it had been on my mind for a while and it was strange seeing how easily he could cry. I'd forgotten that about him.

'Oh really?' he said, and he sniffed. 'I didn't even know. That's okay. I guess this kind of thing gets us all differently. And crying is hard for some men, I guess. I cried for months when my dad died.'

'I know,' I said. 'Mum told me. I sort of felt nothing when you died. But it's not that I didn't love you. It's just that I'd felt grief before, real grief, and I didn't want it again. I refused to let it get me, you know?'

'I know. It's okay. These things are weird and we just feel what we feel.'

'Have you been back to see the house recently?' I asked. 'Can you go there? I mean, can you choose where you haunt or do you just get pulled somewhere by some unknowable force?'

He laughed, 'It doesn't work that way.'

'Hey. Don't laugh. I don't know this stuff, do I? I mean, I didn't even believe in ghosts until you showed up quoting Shakespeare and boaking on my bedroom floor.'

'Yeah, okay,' he said. 'I don't haunt anyone, and I don't get pulled to places. I just get to exist sometimes, for an hour or so, then I'm gone again.'

'Okay,' I said, because what else could I say?

'And yes,' he said. 'I've been back to the house. Most times I come back I'm outside that little yellow house trying to get in. But it's locked.'

'I can't go in there either,' I said. 'It's bad enough that I'm reminded of you when I look in the mirror.'

He just nodded at me and patted me on the shoulder. He probably didn't have anything to say to that. I couldn't think of anything else either, so we just sat in silence and I thought about his house and all the good and bad times there. It's weird, but I sort of knew he was thinking about it too – you know when you can tell someone is having the same thought?

I fell asleep at some point and when I woke up Dad was gone. His smell was gone too, and even the vomit on the ground was gone. I lay awake the rest of the night thinking about that yellow man and his yellow house. And I knew why I'd never gone back, and that I never would.

Alise In Wonderland

Lisa McPeake

'Night night, don't let the bed bugs bite,' he says, as he tucks her into bed and gives her a gentle kiss on the cheek, and a firm, strong, meaningful cuddle. Little Alise wakes up terrified, crying her wee heart out, swaying about and feeling sick, but she's not in her bed, she's cradled in her Mother's arms, on a boat. Everything seems so dull and very stormy.

'Where are we?' Alise asks her Mum.

'We're on a boat Alise, going on holiday to Scotland to visit your Gran and Granda, it's OK, everything will be fine, Mummy's here.'

'Where's Daddy?' Alise asks as she holds on tight, close to her Mother's chest.

That was her last memory, her Father tucking her into her cosy bed. Her Mum didn't answer. Did she hear her, or was she avoiding the question?

Little Alise loved animals and always pined so much for a little dog of her own. With great surprise, as they arrived at Gran and Granda's house they are welcomed by a cute, small ball of fluff, pouncing around, and with much delight and pleasure, Alise is happily distracted from the fact that her Father isn't around.

Three years on and Alise is now seven years old. Her brother is eleven years old and Mum, well she was just Mum. All three are moving into a house of their own after living with Alise's grandparents for the past three years. During that time nobody ever spoke of Alise's Father. If he was mentioned it was like a bad word, he just wasn't to be spoken about.

In their new home Alise and her brother had a bedroom of their own, and Mum had a sofa bed in the living room. She had started dating someone else.

Little Alise, is maturing and not so little now. Her Granda had Multiple Sclerosis, and he was also ageing. Five years down the line, he passed away. Alise and her Granda had such a close bond, he would call her his blue eyed girl. Alise loved to massage her Granda's legs with moisturiser and massage his feet with peppermint foot lotion. This would help the dry skin and the blood circulation in his legs. When he had passed away, Alise wasn't told about it until the next day, she was angry for a long time towards her Mum and brother for that.

Between the age of seven and twelve years old, her brother asked her to lie down and he would sit on top of her and grind his body on her and tell her not to move. He would get her to stick her tongue out and he would rub his tongue on hers. When this first started Alise was told it was a game, but as the years went on Alise did a lot of thinking and wondering more about this game. She realised that this was no game and threatened to tell their Mum about it. But he made it clear that if anyone found out, they would both end up in a home and they would never ever see Mum again, so she kept the secret. She carried the pain and often wondered what life would be like if her Father was around. But now her brother called himself the man of the house. He would take care of them in their new home, just him and Mum and Alise.

Mum was always out now, at raves with the latest boyfriend. She didn't notice that Alise had started to rebel. One day when she was twelve, she found a biscuit tin that was kept in a cupboard where her Mum's clothes were. The tin was stuffed full of all sorts of goodies but not the ones that a child should be trying out. There was cannabis there, and white powder and ten small squares with perforated sides that had small spaceships on them. So she took a chunk of the cannabis, swallowed a tablespoonful of white powder and took five spaceships. She put the rest into her bag and went out to meet her friends.

It wasn't long before Alise was attracting the wrong kind of 'friends'. She was in trouble everywhere. Moved into foster homes to give her Mum respite, three weeks here, three weeks there, there was no home for her anywhere. The only home, and safest one at that, Alise felt was in her own mind, body and soul, her heart was her home. By the age of twelve she was wandering the streets of Glasgow, always looking for someone who would care enough for her. Taking a left, taking a right, wondering which way would be the right way, for her to rest safe and warm at night.

She would sit and beg in the daylight to get enough to have her tummy full. She felt as though she was drowning in a pool, a pool full of pain, and she begged again, but this time it was to score heroin. By the time it was winter Alise was becoming more and more fragile. She thought about getting clean at the age of fifteen. Three years on the streets of Glasgow, Alise had got to know some other people who walked in her shoes, some of the people had soulless shoes. That's what this path of life did to people, it would eat their souls. Alise always found it even more difficult to survive when it was Christmas time. The streets of Glasgow were like a ghost town. She would look at windows with all the colourful lights, windows full of steam, from the home cooking and noises of family laughter and chatter, and the smell of food. Alise always felt more starved at Christmastime, but not for food or a fix, starved from the lack of family love and laughter.

She had a chittering chat to one of her 'friends' who still had some soul left.

'Hey Laura, how are you, you're looking well.'

'I'm good thanks Alise, I'm just out of West Street.'

'West Street?' Alise asks with a confused look upon her face. 'I thought West Street was just for needle exchange.'

'No, no,' says Laura as she laughs. 'It's like a short rehabilitation centre, if you go down and tell them that you want to get clean, they'll assess you, and you either detox in it for three weeks or stabilise.'

'Oh great Laura, I'm so glad I met you there! I need to get clean and a warm bed for a wee while would be great too… I hate this time of year.'

Alise decided to go to West Street and ask for some help. The only problem was Alise knew that it was illegal for her to be prescribed methadone, therefore she worked out a fake date of birth that would make her seem three years older, and of course, Alise used a false name as her social worker and police were looking for her because she was always running away from foster families.

Two weeks into her detox, she was getting three meals a day, reducing off methadone and having a warm roof over her head, with the comfort of a bed. One day Alise was taken to the office. As she walked in, there was two police officers staring at her, her social worker sitting with a smirk, and the manager of West Street.

'Well it's nice to meet you Alise Carson,' the manager says with a smile on his face.

'I'm sorry for lying to you and not telling you my real name and date of birth.'

'That's ok Alise, the police and your social worker would like to speak to you, I've told them how well you have been doing.'

'Ok,' says Alise.

'Do you realise the trouble that you have caused Alise?' asks the cop.

'No, I don't, I'm actually trying to get clean and sort my life out, what's so wrong about that?'

'Well Alise, it's not that you are doing any wrong, but you could have got the manager in here into some serious bother,' says the other cop.

'Why?'

'Because it is illegal to prescribe methadone to someone under the age of eighteen.'

'This is what's going to happen. Since you're already two weeks into your detox, your Mum will be notified of where you are and how well you are doing. A meeting will be held with myself, the police officers, your Mother and the manager. The meeting is for us to discuss how well you have been doing and we will all have a say in whether you should finish your last week or not. If one person says no, then you'll be removed from here and further actions will be taken.'

'Okay then,' Alise replies to her social worker who she really doesn't get on with.

Fortunately for Alise, everyone who had authority unanimously decided to allow her to finish off her last week. During this last week of Alise's detox, all the residents in West Street rehabilitation centre were sent to Brownlee Centre at Gartnavel Hospital to get tested for hepatitis and HIV. Alise felt very confident that all would be OK with her, not that she knew what any of them meant.

Soon afterwards Alise was moved to another foster family, where she was supposed to stay for three weeks. During this time Alise's social worker got in contact with her and told her that she had an appointment at the Brownlee Centre to get her blood test results.

Alise felt very confident that she was well. She was diagnosed with hepatitis C.

She just accepted it that day as she didn't know what it was. Her social worker had then explained to Alise what it actually meant. Well, that was Alise off the rails again. Wondering how she contracted it, wondering *why, why me?* at the age of fifteen, wandering the streets of Glasgow.

Who was Alise, who is Alise?

I am Alise.

My Story: The Yellow and the Blue

Hassan Abdula

I come from a small village in Southern Sudan. I was born and grew up there. Our village is so beautiful, particularly in autumn. It's surrounded with hills on the west and the south part of the village. It has two primary schools and a market, as well as a health centre. People gather every Wednesday. Although the shops are open the whole week, Wednesday is our market day. They come from all the surrounding villages to buy and sell for their everyday needs. Wednesday is not less important than the weekend in Glasgow.

In my village, people do three kinds of work: agriculture, shepherding and trade. They still use camels and donkeys as transport for short journeys and use lorries to travel further, but in general, they are happy. However, the maximum education girls can get is to primary school level because there is no secondary school in the village. Many pregnant women die because there are no ambulances, only big lorries for transport. A lot of patients pass away on the way to the nearest hospital which is a hundred miles away. In addition, the roads are poor. The war started in my state after we demanded development like hospitals and infrastructure. The government targeted educated people because we refused its failed policies. For my safety I had to leave the country.

I went to a city called Hamera Aluz where people can travel to Libya. Service is amazing, zero star! They hit and kick you! We travelled in a big van. I brought some bottles of water and dates with me, and then we moved at night with so many people on top of the van that that if you were lucky enough to get space to sit properly, someone sat on your leg. We had to cross the desert, the big Yellow. The Yellow was always very empty, you can hardly see life on it and it is hard to know where you are. Thousands of people disappeared in the Yellow, and no one knows where. The journey will take ages or days, nobody knows. The desert can take your water, it won't give you shade from very hot sunrise and it tried to put sand in our eyes to stop us from seeing anything. On the third day of our journey, while we were travelling fast, the front tyre got damaged. The driver lost control of the van and people cried because they thought the van was going to overturn. Luckily, we survived and replaced it with a spare tyre. The passengers felt they were in danger. They didn't have enough water and there was no mobile network to call for help.

When we started our journey again, a week later, the engine broke down completely. The driver and his colleagues attempted to repair it, but unfortunately they could not fix it. After two days our food and water ran out. It was hot during the day and cold at night. The driver told us we were safe, anyway. Finally, at night another vehicle came that provided us with some water. It took us to a nearby city. Our clothes were dusty and our skin had dried.

After that, I stayed six months in Libya with a friend. The situation became dangerous. So dangerous that if you go to a shop to get things you might not ever come back, nor would anyone hear any news from you. My friend already had a plan to cross the Blue Sea. He advised me to cross it with him. Perhaps the chances of living became the same whether we stayed, returned or crossed the Blue. So we decided to try it.

We met an agent who arranged travel for my friend and I. We joined other people already in a small boat. It took us to another boat that was not much bigger. There were women and children among them. I met another man from Sudan called Abu Shunb and a woman called Slema. We were in the fish storage area. We couldn't tell night from day. I struggled to breathe and became unconscious for a while. When I came round I found myself out on the boat's deck. They took me back inside, but I tried to remain near a door to breathe.

They took us to another boat that was even bigger but when we were transported across to it, the number of people on board increased. There was a bathroom for all of us and there was food and water, but there wasn't enough. After a few days, the food finished and there was very little water. The crew said the remaining water was just for the children but they will give us a cup a day. People started fighting each other. Abu Shunb was lying near the bathroom's door and he became annoyed with it. He pulled off the door of the bathroom and threw it away. Slema wanted to use it but there was no door.

'Why did you pull off the door and throw it away? You are a terrible man,' she said.

'You are a rude woman. Shut up or otherwise I will throw you in the Blue,' he said.

Two men made a new door with a piece of cloth and she was able to use the bathroom again then.

We began to dream about water. There was nothing more precious than water. I had a bottle of water but I couldn't drink because if other people saw it they would make me give it to them. If I refused, I would be at risk, so at night I wanted to drink my water, but unfortunately I found the bottle was completely empty. I thought, oh my goodness, am I dreaming? I shouted 'Who drank my water?' but nobody spoke because they were so thirsty.

There were two enemies besides the Yellow – the air and the waves. When sunset came, the wind started to blow and the waves were like mountains, taking the boat up and down. People were crying. The waves led the boat any direction they wanted. Every day we travelled miles and miles and at night the waves returned us miles and miles, so we were running out of fuel for nothing.

Nothing became more important than water. Even life felt less important than water. The crew were nice to people and they said we were close to reaching somewhere, there was nothing to be worried about. They treated the women, children and sick patients as best as they could. We kept travelling and returning. The navigation was completely controlled by the waves for many days. The crew told us we would only get half a glass of water otherwise we would face catastrophe. Luckily, a giant ship was travelling nearby and they saw us and came near to us with a small boat. They threw us bottles of water and we were relieved. They really helped us and called for rescue. We waited one more day for help, and then another big ship came and took us to Italy.

When I was travelling through Italy I noticed its wonderful mountains and the fantastic tunnels under these mountains. I passed through a small island called Messina that was quiet. It had fascinating buildings on its mountains and the streets over the hills were decorated with trees and flowers. It was quite warm and you couldn't stay long in the sun. I spent two days there. There were great moments. I saw lots of people on cruises and tourists taking photos. I saw a group of men wearing black jackets and black trousers. They rode big motorbikes making lots of noise. I thought they were the Italian Mafia. I went to the island's harbour and saw a lot of ships coming from different countries.

The island's people were very nice and friendly, however, they did not like speaking any foreign language so it was difficult to communicate with them. I went to a bar to buy some soft drinks. I asked the staff, 'Do you speak English or Arabic?' and the woman replied, 'No English', so I used sign language. I went up close to items then I said, 'I want that!' It was an easy way to communicate.

The island's buses often travelled at night. I booked a bus to Torino. We spent the whole night on the road. We arrived into Roma in the morning. We had breakfast and a couple of hours then we changed over buses. Again, a new journey started. The bus passed over bridges. There was lovely scenery and we went through amazing tunnels. We stopped in Genoa and we took short break. There were farms near the road and forests. The driver of the bus said something that I didn't understand so I asked a girl sat next to me and she said the bus wouldn't stop for a break again until Turino.

I was so eager to see Juventus's city and its stadium. The city has a unique architecture. There are drawings painted on the sides of the buildings with different colours. I left to go Ventimiglia City by train near the French border. I took a train to Paris. It is the most beautiful city I have ever seen so far. And then I went to Calais where the UK's border is.

I stayed two months in the 'jungle' camp and then I came to the UK. Immigrants were facing all kinds of risk. It was dangerous to travel and if you survived the journey you still faced an unknown future if your application of asylum was rejected.

Many immigrants are qualified. I came to Glasgow last year, luckily my application was successful. I am very grateful to the UK. I have lived in many different parts of Glasgow but now I live in the East End. I like Glasgow and the people are very nice. I like libraries and I like voluntary work. The most exciting work I have ever done is working as a volunteer at the Homeless World Cup in Glasgow. Now, I work in a charity shop. I have a science degree and I used to work for a pharmaceutical company back in my country.

My ambition is to complete a postgraduate degree at Glasgow University and then I will be more qualified to work in the pharmaceutical companies here or become a lecturer there.

A Bit of Kit

May 7th, 1996

Jacqui Cathcart

When I take a bit of kit
I get a buzz, a right good hit
Can't sit up straight on the couch
I close my eyes I've got to gouch.

I feel a warm glow inside of me
Now I can shut out reality
Face the real world, what no way
This is much better any day.

Problems that you had before
Are not an issue anymore
The phone, the gas, the rent
Will have to wait, the money is spent.

The only problem that is real
Is getting drugs so you can feel
Good enough to face each day
To deal with life in every way.

It's so great at first, then it's so sad
Didn't know that you could feel so bad
Your body crying out for drugs each day
You've got to have them, come what may.

Just wish I knew how it would be
A life full of shit and total misery
Thirteen years of hurt and so much pain
Living life on the edge, I must be insane.

Wish I could get back to what I used to be
Just living a normal life being drug free
But it does get harder as the years go by
Giving up won't be easy but I'll have to try.

Every person has their fair share
Of hurt and pain and desolate despair
Being an addict is hard there is no doubt
But surely there's got to be some way out.

The bad points outweigh the good
I should try to stop, I really should
'Cos when the buzz is so long gone
It's hard without drugs to carry on.

Put my life into perspective now
Got to give up though I don't know how
It'll be hard I know but I've got to try
'Cos if I don't stop soon I know I'll die.

They Gave It To Me

Alan Bissett

'They gave it to me,' the man in the doorway said, tugging at his sleeping bag, the shell fabric of which gleamed with newness and raindrops. 'And this jacket.' He thumbed the hood of his padded waterproof and Mark looked up at the logo of the store the man was huddled before, its jagged crests signifying hillwalks. The December night was freezing, sleet-driven, the kind that turned a sleeping-bag into a basic mammal warmth.

'That's so good of them,' said Mark, smiling at the man through the sleet. 'To give you a sleeping bag? Usually all they do is move homeless folk on.'

The man shook his head, deep within his hood, and blinked slowly, then his eyes flickered to the styrofoam cup, the pennies scattered within, as though to say: *I've been chatting to you for over a minute now. Are you going to give me some money?*

Mark ruffled in his pockets and found no change. Embarrassment coursed through him. He took out his wallet and saw only a tenner. His mind paused, frowned, recalibrated: there was no way he was going to leave the man nothing, and what was a tenner to someone in secure employment with a roof over his head every night? Two, three pints that he'd forget as soon as they were urinated out of his system? Besides, this store had given the man a *free sleeping bag.*

Mark stuffed the tenner into the styrofoam cup before he could give himself time to reconsider, and the man's rheumy eyes creased. 'Cheers, pal.'

'No problem.' Mark stood. 'Good luck.' He waved the man goodbye, hunching his shoulders against the flat splashes of sleet, and headed further down Sauchiehall Street towards the train station.

Around him, the display windows of shops gleamed – Barbour jackets, plush scarves, knee-length boots – while from inside the darkness of doorways cocoons shifted and coughed.

The mannequins, he noticed, were better dressed than the people. Once on the train the sweat trapped beneath the layers of his clothes began to cool. Mark took out his phone and went straight to Facebook. *They gave it to me.* The simplicity of that. The generosity. There among the commuters – thick with steaming coats, legs pressed together in the warmth – something in Mark's soul glowed. He typed into his Status Update box:

Shout out to this store, who not only let a homeless guy kip in their doorway but donated him a sleeping bag and jacket!

Realising he hadn't taken a picture – it would've felt rude to ask the man to pose – Mark found a stock image of the shop from the company's website and clipped it to his Status Update. Then he pressed Publish.

He slid his phone into his pocket and rested his head against the drizzly train-window, looking out at the vastness of Glasgow, the myriad lights of its bars and clubs and restaurants and cars and buses and boozers and schools and banks and tenements and blank, dreaming council schemes, and he thought about all the things he couldn't do, the thousands of people he couldn't help, before the lulling of the train rocked him into a dreamless, thin sleep.

When he woke, jerked back to life by the tannoy announcing Larkhall, he reached for his phone to check the time, noticing blearily that his Facebook page was alive. *56 shares. 384 likes.* He scrolled through the comments

That's the spirit of Glasgow!

So nice that a store would do that. Shame on the others.

Kindness is alive and well!

That story cheered me up!

Gotta pity someone sleeping out in this. Be giving that shop my custom from now on.

and dozens more like them. Pleasure welled at the corner of Mark's eyes; the message passed forwards, a touching of hands in the dark.

He stepped onto the platform as the wind picked up, hurling the sleet into his face. He headed towards home, watching the Shares and the Likes and the Comments scroll in, and did not feel the cold, not for a second.

By the time he was opening the front door of his flat, kicking the slush from his boots, the Comments had changed.

Fake.

Calling bullshit on this.

Don't see anyone homeless in this photo!

Do you happen to work for this chain?

This guy's just chasing Likes and Friends.

Mark's cheeks were burning, partly from his cold skin hitting the warmth of his flat, partly from the anger. Each sentence landed like a Molotov cocktail amongst the communal joy.

He threw off his coat and was replying before his arse even hit the couch, then that was him for the rest of the night, fighting off the sneering, sour nobodies who'd come scuttling from the far corners of Facebook to take his story down. Mark found himself tapping at his phone righteously, as the wind outside the flat hooted derision, but for every comment he replied to another appeared, like a severed Hydra head, then another, then another, until one of them made him stop typing and stare at the screen.

My pal's the manager of that shop. Just phoned him and he knows nothing about this.

Mark stood and paced the living room, actually paced, the way he'd seen people in films do, something he'd always presumed to be fake until he'd felt this particular coiling in his gut, this twitching in his feet. *468 Shares. 391 Likes*. But the replies were coming in to that last post quickly:

Knew it. He's made this up.

Shops don't give out free gear,
too good to be true.

Screw this guy, using the homeless
to draw attention to himself.

You're sad.

'But,' Mark said to the phone, as though the thousands of people who'd seen and shared his post could hear him, 'He *told* me.'

They gave it to me.

He replayed the film footage in his memory: the sleet drifting between them again, the guy thumbing his sleeping bag and Mark looking up at the shop logo. 'They' had meant the store, surely? The man hadn't corrected him, after all, but—

But.

Was it feasible 'they' had meant a homeless charity? Some nameless passers-by? Had Mark made a false assumption? After all, shops *didn't* give out free gear. That's what made it so remarkable. Had Mark simply wanted to believe so much in that moment of goodness – on a frigid winter night, faced with a tragedy he was helpless to prevent – that he'd convinced himself the incredible was credible, that High Street store managers were now taking it upon themselves to keep the homeless warm?

Mark switched off his phone, which was pinging scorn at him every few seconds, and lay back on the couch. His mind roamed across the lunar surface of the ceiling artex as the flat resounded with silence.

After a while he rose and went to the kitchen, where he made himself a microwave meal for one.

By the next morning, the winter sky was an expanse of azure, the stillness of the air a pleasure to breathe.

Mark walked to the train station reading the Facebook comments (*9013 shares, 17,79 Likes*), many trilling with joy, others with claws, calling him a liar. But among the blitz of thumbs aloft and angry emojis a comment caught his eye

Erika, was this you??

and the reply from 'Erika Hamilton':

Course it was lol

He clicked on Erika Hamilton's profile, as the train slid to a halt on the platform before him and the grey ranks of commuters shuffled on. *Born: Motherwell. Attends: Strathclyde University. Works: Activate Hillwalking Store, Sauchiehall Street.*

Half an hour later, Mark was standing outside the shop, breathing in that chilly, sharp air and wondering. There was no homeless man in the doorway now, of course. No-one to corroborate this but Erika Hamilton.

He stepped inside. The heater blast welcomed him. Around him were dotted empty tents, like the ghosts of an abandoned camp. Blank faced figures posed in the latest hiking gear. A shop assistant looked up from a knot he was untying in the guy rope of a display tent, then strode over to Mark. 'Can I help you?'

Mark coughed, noticing the man's badge. 'GARY. STORE MANAGER. 'Uh. Is there an Erika who works here?'

Gary glanced to an upper floor, where a young woman was folding some scarves. 'Can I ask who's looking for her?'

'Yes,' said Mark, 'I'm, uh—' His mind emptied. 'I'm… a journalist.'

'A journalist?' Gary's tone took on a firmer quality. 'For who?'

'The, uh Daily Record. There's a story circulating on Facebook that you gave a sleeping bag and jacket to a homeless guy.'

Gary sighed. 'Yes, I heard about this. We don't know anything about it.'

'Could I talk to Erika anyway?'

Gary's head cocked to the side. 'Why Erika?'

Why Erika indeed? Mark fumbled in his head for the character of Daily Record Journalist.

'My, um, source—'

'Source?'

'—thought she might know something about it.'

Gary frowned. This, clearly, was not good news. He tilted his chin upwards towards the mezzanine, looking at Erika for a second before he called her name.

Erika turned. Mark beckoned her with his hand.

As she descended the stairs towards them, Gary talked '…we let the guy sleep in the doorway, yes, but there's no way Head Office would let me away with giving him free kit, you understand.'

Mark was nodding but barely listening. As Erika approached, he summoned images of her reading *The Guardian*, silently fuming about poverty statistics, or on a march against austerity, placard jabbing at the air, or bending to the homeless man he'd spoken to the previous night, handing him the bundle, and whispering, '*Don't tell anyone….*'

'…I mean, it's not that we don't *want* to help these people, but we get known for giving out sleeping bags we'd have every homeless guy in Glasgow forming a queue outside our door!'

Erika stopped in front of them, hair pulled back into a pony-tail, her expression blank and awaiting instruction.

'Erika,' said Gary, 'Do you know anything about this story doing the rounds on Facebook?' There was a prickly underlay of warning in Gary's voice, or so Mark felt anyway.

Erika blinked and looked at Mark standing there silently. 'Are you from the police?'

'No,' said Mark, 'I'm a reporter with the Daily Record. Just wanted to check the story out with you.'

'Says he's got a source,' Gary added, folding his arms and staring at Erika.

She glanced from Gary to Mark then back to Gary again. The music from the tannoy rolled in the atmosphere between them, a folk song from the Seventies which Mark vaguely recognised.

Erika shook her head. 'Nothing to do with me.'

Mark swallowed. 'Are you sure?' He tried to signal with his eyes: *I believe in you. You're a good person.*

Erika took a deep breath and Mark thought he saw something gather behind her eyes, like a bird briefly lifting its wings, before it settled again. 'Aye saw that thing on Facebook, likes. But that's all I know about it.'

Do this for me. Please. Tell me the truth.

Gary shrugged and opened his hand to Mark. 'We can't help you, I'm afraid.'

Mark pursed his lips.

'Thanks, Erika,' said Gary, 'You can get back to work now.'

'Sure.' Erika's gaze lingered on Mark for just a second, before her turning head dragged it away and she trotted obediently back up the stairs.

Gary put his hands in his pockets. 'Just some daftie spreading nonsense on the internet, I'd say. Sorry your time's been wasted.'

'Yup,' said Mark, looking at Erika's back, at the way her shoulders slumped when she reached the table of scarves, robotically picking them up and folding them.

'Have a good day,' said Gary.

Mark exited the store and went back into the stream of bodies in Sauchiehall Street heading to work, heads down, mouths tight, as the phone in his pocket pinged over and over again.

Clyde

Eric Hamilton

So many songs and poems have been written about other bodies of water but I've never ever heard one about me. I am the mighty River Clyde and I've been flowing along every day for as long as rain has fallen on the hills that are on either side of my banks. It was when man began to use me in many ways that I changed so much. The earliest came when I was shallowest and at the low tide you could wade from one side to the other.

When the religious men came the first of many buildings were erected on my banks. Theirs was a special massive stone edifice with a spire on top to get as close to their god as possible. Early morning sun shone from upriver and the monks would come to sit by my side and commune with their god. These were good people and never dumped anything into me that would damage me in any way. Not like what was coming soon.

My sides were brought closer together and stuff so nasty and poisonous was poured into me that my friends the fish no longer came up from the ocean to where their ancestors had always come to lay their eggs in clean fresh water. Huge wooden boats would wait downstream for the high tide when they were towed by rowing boats on the flow of the incoming tide. It was where this tidal flow got as far as it could that the city of Glasgow was to grow.

As all the islands were now no more my banks were enclosed by stone and wood. Still they poisoned me with their rubbish and their unwanted leftovers, their chemicals and their industrial waste. They thought as I was such a mighty river that the rainfall would be enough to carry everything downstream and out to sea.

Now ships were coming in on every tide and would tie up to be unloaded. Tobacco and sugar warehouses appeared and as the traffic got heavier and heavier they cut out great basins which meant more boats could be tied up and unloaded and cargoes could be stored in the warehouses that were built around the docks. The human waste poured into pipes and sewers and down to my banks and it was taken out to deeper water on bigger boats and dumped where it was thought it would do no harm.

But the money flowed into the coffers of many in the Glaswegian Merchants and through taxes into the corporation of Glasgow. As Glasgow grew around both sides of me, ways to get from one bank to the other were going on from boats, tunnels and finally bridges.

As the city grew most of the streams that joined me were put into pipes and covered over. As ships got bigger and bigger, keeping the passageway for them to get upstream as far as possible became so costly and troublesome that a new port named Port Glasgow was created way downstream. Boats were getting bigger and all the docks were no longer needed as they were just too small now.

Then when men were fighting one another far away, from my water on a moonlit night from the east and using my reflection as a guide they came. What seemed to be great birds dropped bombs one after the other for the three nights of the full moon. They bombed the shipyards and the homes of the people who worked in these yards. So many humans, but they rebuilt.

Rain kept on falling and my tributaries kept flowing into me. Now after the humans had fought for years the shipbuilding moved to other great rivers in other countries. The docks and shipbuilders and the wharfs and all the industry that once was on both my banks from the limit of the tidal reach for miles further downstream was now gone. Left to dereliction, from so much to so little. There was an upside to this, my waters were getting cleaner and cleaner and more of my friends the fish returned. A few to start with, but steadily their numbers grew. How life finds a way, such a mystery.

As the waters became cleaner and no boats came to offload their cargoes, docks which took so much effort to create were filled in to make more land alongside the banks.

Once the land was created came modern buildings, museums and homes for people and these people didn't do now what the ones that came before did, they treated me well. I became full of life again, and as they no longer dredge a channel to let their big ships come up to be offloaded, sandbars are forming and at low tide these can be seen. The wildlife and nature that had been missing for so long has all come back.

Perhaps the songs will become louder now.

The Margins

To Jacqui

AK Thaysen

another little pharaoh shuffling past
another copper tossed to a sinking rock –
        history always has business
        on the other side of town

scissored out of his recollection
once again, your name's pasted
in a book you've never skimmed
and have no access to –
        you survive by napping in the yellowed margins,
        the shadowed stoops,
        the peripheries of other, more autonomous humans
who wave charts of untraumatic childhoods
like baguettes under the arm

they're blowing these bubbles as long as possible
        unaware that breath has been purchased so dearly;
that, in an instant, it could leave them
walls pulled away
threads of words
        unraveling sounds
        unraveling every structure
        that separates *them* from *us*

your breath, in contrast,
appearing only in a time of great need,
grateful for any opportunity to compose,
though now your options
are limited to
        scrawling on an envelope

as you lie between your boyfriend's bed and the window
crouched small
– a poem to drown the shouting
coming from the other room

…can you imagine a space of your own devising?
with enough solitude, encouragement
enough blank pages
to transpose *your* 1st person
to *her* 3rd person?
(– does the bus go there?)

make that space the shape
of the hole you feel inside you
and give it the frame
your father once held you in

the trouble being
the electric beats of your heart
must be measured
before they are divided
by the sharp pain
of pneumonic breath

a rhythm of wind chimes
to build around

Lost Generation

Stephen Murphy

14th July 2016

'Murder, you are murder Ricky, were ur ye for fuck sake, ma taxis phoned' Mick Roberts said into his mobile.

'Two minutes mate, passing the high court.'

'Should always run past that place Rick, its murder in there pal.'

'Aye right, wae this fucking leg' Ricky dinked the phone.

Murder was the last thing on Richard Mullan's mind as he passed Glasgow's High Court, turning onto Clyde Street passing Hope House hostel on his way to the lane before the Clutha pub, Salvation Army run from 1934 the ninety-six room hostel was now closed down.

'Murder place was fucking murder, its dejafuckingvu' Ricky said aloud. At thirty-eight through drink and a myriad of family problems he found himself homeless, and within a week in Hope House was injecting and selling heroin again. People may have found hope in there at one time, safe to say it was lost when Ricky got there and they clearly never regained it. In 2009 in fact, just as he got there a major campaign was launched backed by the Police, Councillor Gordon Mathieson and local tenants to have it closed ASAP.

Ricky had two good pals and Mick was one of them. Mick was one of those guys who took life in his stride Ricky started selling heroin with him shortly after meeting in Hope House. Mick was from the other side of the city, a Gorbals boy, sound, and they just clicked, trusted each other 100 per cent and that doesn't happen often. Mick had done time for a murder when he was younger and been in and out since for car offences, mainly having no licence. They had moved on. Mick met a bird, and after initial help from a staff member, Tam one of the good guys, Ricky remembered him, fancy a game a fitbaw, a long road, with a lot of detours and heartache in between, Ricky had ended up clean. Ever since they had kept in touch Ricky had visited him in BarL and Mick didn't forget things like that. Ricky enjoyed them as well as both of them were clean and it cemented the friendship for life that was going on seven years.

But here they were again Mick still selling and Ricky on his arse.

'Right pal here, gub these' Mick said, 'and forget the money.'

'Sure' said Ricky.

'Aye cool, listen am gien this a by for a while, somefucker OD'd the other night, rumour gaun aboot it was ma kit a don't need the hassle mate, fucking coppers sniffing aboot, am gien you the run if ye want, a wiz due a break anyway.'

'Fuck aye, a don't know Mick.'

'There's a minimum grand a week here for you Ricky, and its a canter, hauf an oor mate twice a day, even less, ye wid'ny be waiting oan yersel, a wid'ny gie it tae anycunt else.'

'Ha fucking ha, am pure skint anaw mate, al let you know, cool?'

'Who wiz it emday we know?' asked Ricky.

'Wan a they Mitchels.'

'Aw fuck!' Ricky's eyes went up, 'that's aw ye need, wit wan? there's squaads a them.'

'The ugly wan, couldny care less pal' Mick said.

'That narrows it doon for fuck sake, theyre aw ugly bastards.'

'Fuckall tae dae wae me anywae, ma punters are aw haun picked, and listen it dizny matter tae me wan wae or the other its your earner here pal, in fact ad rather ye goat yersel back aff it aw the gither you were daen fucking brilliant there. How's Des doing by the way?'

'Des, aye he's daen great, up at Pheonix last a heard huv'ny seen him right enough.'

'There's ma taxi, let me know ok, here, you need a haircut by the way.'

'Aw cheers pal, catch ye, Versace!'

As Ricky walked along the Trongate headed for Queen Street Station turning up Albion Street passing The Spoon café, two clearly gay individuals were outside it with leaflets, one dressed and looking like the dart player Peter Wright without thc spikey hair, although this guy could have carried that off no problem confidence oozed out of him, promoting the LGBTI community through the Homeless World Cup football competition taking place in George Square that week. The whole city had embraced the event. With over five hundred players men and women from some seventy countries across the globe, and for that week, George Square was transformed into the most inspiring place on the planet. There was even sixty-foot-high murals on the side of buildings of players past and present dotted all over the city, a huge undertaking took on at short notice, but Glasgow had delivered as Glasgow does, with class.

'Gaun yersel pal' Ricky said, quickly taking a leaflet and skirting round them, without breaking stride.

LGBTI. 'Fucking I'. The 'I' was a new one on Ricky maybe they are a five a side team he thought stupidly, mind you there's nae I in team, he laughed at his own poor joke.

Heading along Ingram Street he could hear the tannoy announcing teams onto the pitch, National Anthems were being played, it sounded tremendous and it was dry today a bonus for Glaswegians officially the wettest city in the UK, according to the Chase, and the monsoons the day before. But he wasn't going to walk through he had fucked up and people who helped him get clean were involved. Glasgow's recovery community had come together and linking with Glasgow Life and the Big Lottery had provided over one hundred volunteers for the event, an opportunity priceless to some.

'Richard Mullan!' he recognised the voice first it took a split second before it fell into place that the guy standing outside the front entrance of the City Chambers and looking a million dollars, was his best pal Des, mad as a brush, never stopped talking. At one time Ricky and Des were inseparable and right then and there it magnified his own fuck up, and need to get aff this stuff he said to himself for the millionth time.

The last time Ricky had seen Des he was a wreck, broken, he had been yanked off his medication after losing it with a receptionist who had looked down her nose at addicts and most people for years. The police were called and that was that seventeen years on medication, a two minute rant and he was on his own! it happens. Clearly strung out and in need of something pronto, he never asked Ricky just put twenty quid in his hand with the faint promise to go to the Crisis Centre and get an assessment done. That was a year ago. Ricky was two years clean then.

'WOW Des Quinn for fuck sake mate look at ye, yer staunin there like Paddy McGuiness in Phoenix Nights' Des had a confident air about him Ricky hadn't seen for years and it was amazing. Getting into recovery could have that effect Ricky knew.

The handshake and bear hug that followed, spoke volumes.

'I knew I was gony see you the day, I just fucking knew it, been thinking aboot you aw morning ya bastard, and bang yer there, aw Rick its brilliant tae see ye mate this is fucking amazing init' he gestured to the Square.

'Brilliant tae see me look at YOU! wits aw this' he motioned to the ID badge.

'Am a volunteer, but am a VIP wan so am in here wae the city fathers hey hey.'

'VI fucking P eh.'

'A know.'

'Ha ha ya dancer ye, on ye fucking go, brilliant mate, a canny believe how fucking healthy you look compared…'

'Tell me aboot it Rick, fuck ye think id hit rock bottom when ye saw me last, a still hid another few flairs tae go doon mate, when a goat intae that Crisis Centre they telt me a widny huv lasted another week, a wiz dying mate, simple. A collapsed the week before ma body was just chucking it! Signed myself oot right enough.' All the time he was bouncing from foot to foot, never still, eyes alive.

'Ya muppet Des, fuck sake, I knew you were bad mate.'

'A went up and goat linked intae that Phoenix day programme you were at, and I huvny looked back since. Honest mate they bastards done me a favour when they took me aff that av git energy tae burn and am thinking clear as a bell.'

'Fucking proud o ye bro, you sound on the ball, for a change anyway.' Ricky laughed, 'Hows yer wee Maw daen?'

'Brilliant, shes over the fucking moon, every time she sees me her eyes light up.'

'Her boy back int she, fuck you look amazing mate! still canny believe it.'

'Go up and see her she always asks aboot you for some reason.'

'A wull, a wull.'

'Al tell her then so ye better. By the way Ricky, I was on the telly for this thing last week.'

'Aye right yar, the telly, telly' Rickys head went back the way.

'Aye fuck sake ye know that square thing sits in the living room wae pictures oan it.'

'Aye awright smart arse, nae kidding?'

'Aye honest it was on STV Glasgow but, ye know that shitey channel naecunt watches, was only for ten seconds but it was live.'

'Live, fuckin live, on ye go the Dessie boy.'

'Wiz bottling it anaw mate, ma wee Maw, fuck you'd think a wiz on River City for fuck sake she's telling the post office queue.'

'Right anaw wee Sadie.'

'Naw mate she asked if a wizny interested in drama the other day a mean cmon fucking drama.'

'Looking for an agent.'

'Good yin, youre no gony believe this wan either av signed up for a creative writing course through this, some Legacy thing, am intae everything mate.'

'Aye yer right a don't believe ye, Des ye need tae be able tae spell first for that pal.'

'Cheeky bastard Mullan! so wit the fuck happened tae you' Des said.

'Aw mate a wiz daen great there as ye know then that treatment for the HEP C stopped me dead, the boredom kicked in, don't know mate, a hid been through the services your daen the noo, then that online betting done ma heid in.'

'The gambling, fuck' said Des.

'Torture absolute torture Des. Fuck I put sixty quid on the Chinese woman's volleyball team wan time, it wiz three in the fucking morning, couldny sleep, ma heid was up my arse, too easy couple a buttons, and they got beat the slant eyed bastards. Then wan day a bought a bag and that wiz it, darts team, straight in double top, noo am six month down the line.'

'Yer no back oan a script are ye?' Des asked warily.

'Naw am a fuck, twenty-three years in a coma was enough tha done me that stuff.'

'Yer brand fucking new then jist get back in aboot it for fuck sake, tell you Ricky id fucking ban that to anybody under thirty, gie people a chance to have a fucking life first, it was murder coming aff it. You twenty three year me seventeen, tell ye we are a lost generation pal.'

England v Norway the tannoy announced.

'Is Iceland in it?' Ricky said, they both just folded into laughter.

One week earlier England had been humbled by lowly ranked Iceland in the Euros, and no one in Scotland was for letting it go anytime soon, or until our own next fiasco which was in the post as Scotland are consistent, especially when it comes to minnows.

'A know poor Woy eh wosing to Iceland' said Des.

'A pure wiberty, Des mate.'

'That fanny Joe Hart wit a legend that boys turned oot tae be eh' Des laughed.

'Love the guy, Knight im, aw, he is pure shite, wit a gilbert' said Ricky.

'Brilliant mate,' Des said holding his stomach.

There the two pals were outside Glasgows hub of power, in stitches and it felt tremendous.

'So who's in there' Ricky asked.

'In there, aw naebody really I was talking to that Michael Jamieson boy though you know the swimmer, Commonwealth Games finished second, poster boy fae Bishopbriggs, nice guy right enough, doon tae earth, know.'

'Aye the guy that got a silver at the Olympics, boy wiz fucking brilliant, Scottish so a remember it well know wit a mean?'

'Fuck did he that's right so he did aye, him, he looks a bit lost the boy he overtrained he was telling me. Trying to get into coaching the weans noo or the telly commentating, I told him I knew a good hitman if he wanted they two fucking Andy clowns took oot.'

'Is that it?'

'Mate am at the back next to the tea there wiz some UEFA guy there gibbering away I couldny make oot a word he was saying, but he seemed pleased wae himself anywae.'

'Nae wonder probably oan a fortune the fucker.'

'By the way Jan and Aileen fae Pheonix are in there the day wae the troops, go and see them,' Des said.

'Naw al go up the road and see them mate. Wit aboot big Kev he still trying tae play fitbaw?'

'"Injured"' they both chimed and laughed.

'Been there and done it the big yin, like big Kev,' said Ricky.

'Aw mate he took us doon tae Thistles 5s pitch, wit a gem a fitbaw, first time in years mate, fucking loved it.'

'Brilliant, brilliant pal.'

'Listen, make sure ye go up.'

'I will, right am gony get off pal, tell wee Aileen a was asking ok.'

'Cool bro be good, and am telling ma maw you'll be up, soon.'

'By the way Quinn you look fucking brilliant' said Ricky pointing his finger like a gun as he walked away.

'A know' Des said.

'Here Des, is that swimmer worth a few quid?' Ricky shouted.

As evidenced by Dessie the Crisis Centre worked miracles, not as many or as often as Cadogan Street where rumour has it the DWP are going to transform the building into a pilgrimage site, the Crisis Centre already has that status within the recovery community, these are genuine miracles with real peoples help, people like Marlene Johnson, Stephen Craig and Tricia Tracey all following on from the people before. Opened in 1994 through pressure from parents and grandparents concerned about the scourge of drugs, that had took hold of their communities in the eighties and decimated families in the process, working to help addicts or people with any social problems 24/7 to overcome their issues and help them back into society.

He knew he was going to have to go back there to go forwards he couldn't kid himself any more that he was only dabbling, he had a problem a big one especially if he started selling again and had a few quid, as nice a change as that would be and tempting as it was, he knew he would be bang in trouble and he also knew he couldn't chance another round with coke. He would let Mick know.

The next day with Mick's phone on voicemail Ricky went through the door of the Crisis Centre, all the way there debating with himself, a grand a week or clean a grand a week or clean to be greeted by Tam the worker from Hope House. 'Richard Mullan' he heard again. 'I was just talking about you.'

An hour later Ricky was told Mick Roberts had been attacked and killed outside his mother's house in the Gorbals area the previous night, the police were treating it as murder.

Going Shopping

Nikki Cameron

You walk this city as if you know it. You walk with confidence. You know how this world works. You've lived here for years, safe and secure. When you leave your home to go shopping for the day, you lock the door securely behind you. You are a responsible home owner. You take care of your property. You pay your council tax and your name is on the electoral register. You care for your local neighbourhood. It is a good neighbourhood with neat gardens and new cars perfectly parked. You walk to the end of your road to take the bus. There's always a bus coming along and it is the green thing to do, taking a bus shows that you care for the environment. It will take you straight to the shops and if you spend so much that you are weighed down by the glossy bags you can always take a taxi home.

While you journey on the bus you have time to catch up on the news on your smartphone. The news is very troubling. The world is frightening. There are people in the world who want to take away everything you have. You cannot name these people but you know they exist. They are blamed every day in the newspaper you read. You are told everyday by your friends that the world is not safe. There are people who do not work, who do not save, who do not look after their families. These people want what you have. They want you to pay for it. They have come to your country to take it away from you.

You have always voted. You know that it is important and when you consider where to place your cross you take into account what is best for the country. If the government looks after you, then they must be doing the right thing for the whole country because you are a model citizen. You worked hard and paid your taxes and looked after your family and saved wisely.

You are not racist. You and your friends agree on that every Tuesday when you meet for lunch. And you think that people who are ill – really ill and not pretending – should be helped if they cannot work. But there are too many people who are lazy and drug addicts and think that you should look after their families. You and your friends agree that the charities must be exaggerating the numbers of families that use food banks. You have never met anyone who needed to use a food bank and the government you elected will always help those that really need help. You were shocked that your own minister at your own church asked you to help, in a street so close to your home.

Really, you know there are serious issues but the government has to make difficult choices and it must in the end do the very best for the ones who work hard and pay their taxes and save and look after their own families. You never needed help and you wouldn't ask the government anyway and there have been times when you struggled but you still worked hard and now quite rightly you've earned everything you have.

The bus journey is nearly over but you have time to check your emails and you note in particular the offer from a holiday company suggesting a two week cruise in the Mediterranean. You consider that it might be suitable for January; some sunshine would get you through a long cold winter.

You arrive at the city centre. Everyone is busy. They are walking between shops and purchases. Some already are laden with shiny bags. You visit the shops here almost every day. You know what is in the windows and you are aware of what is the latest fashion. You care about your appearance, you like to look good and you choose to get rid of clothes you consider are outdated. You always give the clothes to your local charity shop. That makes you feel good to know that clothes of such quality can be used to such good purpose. So you enjoy the feeling of shopping.

You walk along the street. The sun is so bright today, though there is rain forecast for later. But you always have that small yellow umbrella that your granddaughter gave you for your last birthday handy at the bottom of your handbag. You won't get caught out by the weather. And if you do you have a book with you to read in your favourite coffee shop for later. You notice that dress is still in the window from earlier in the week and it's been reduced and you consider it again. It would be perfect for that dinner you are going to next month and you could get more use from it if you go on that cruise in January. It would go so well with the new shoes you got last week. You get closer to the window and you look at the dress fitted perfectly to the mannequin. The entire outfit is exquisite, the fabric folds and flows around the shape of the model and you realise that there is a small detail of sparkle and you imagine dancing on a ship to your favourite music and the gold dust catching the eyes of the officers. Every detail of the scene in your mind is as clear and as sharp as the reality of the world you stand in now. Your home ground.

But you don't see it do you? Even now as you stand at the window with the beautiful dress in it, with the sparkle of gold dust, you see nothing. You will walk these streets a thousand times, buy a thousand shiny things and you will never see it.

Over there in the doorway. Barely a metre away from your sparkly, shiny dress and shoes.

Look.

See the person that is completely still at the edge of the dancing feet.

Look. Don't turn away. You will see this. You will not walk away.

She can't see you either. Your world is as invisible to her as she is to you. So you're safe to look. Sit on that bench, there in the middle of the street. You can watch her. She was there all the time you were staring in the window. You walked past her earlier. You didn't see her then and she had long ago stopped holding out her hand to any one passing by. She's taken a few kicks, a good number of curses and about £2 in change.

And she'll be dead in an hour.

So why not take a moment? It's a privilege few people get; to be there when someone takes their last breath. Don't be scared, the dress will still be there.

She's small and pushed in tight against the wall. She doesn't have many breaths left. Be respectful. Imagine she's another human being at the most human moment of any life – the final moment.

She last slept in a bed a week ago. It wasn't a great bed but it was warm and she got three good meals a day. It was in a prison cell. So she really isn't like you at all, is she? A year ago she was sentenced because she wandered into a supermarket brandishing an axe which she then threw at a display of sanitary towels. She resisted arrest and punched the policeman. She had also been shoplifting. Tampax. Try having a period when you're homeless.

She can't remember why she had the axe with her but she ended up in prison. She wasn't charged with the shoplifting, they never mentioned the Tampax. She spent more time inside because she assaulted the prison officers. She can't remember why she did that either. She settled to prison life after a while; you always wake up to a dozen friends round about you when you're inside. It was the only time she could remember not feeling lonely.

Six months before the incident with the axe, she'd been in hospital. Diagnosed with depression, she had tried to kill herself with an overdose of sleeping tablets. When she got out of hospital she didn't want to go home and moved into a flat with a friend. They shared everything – every shot of heroin, every joint and every adulterated Valium tablet.

A year before the incident with the axe she'd been living with her family in a street not very far away from where you live. She was doing well at school. She was young and bright and she went shopping a lot too. One night she went out with a group of friends to a party. She got drunk and a nice boy who she hadn't seen before offered to get her home safely. She was found a couple of days later wandering the streets on the other side of the city. The head injuries she had sustained left her deaf in one ear and prone to panic attacks.

You can't see her arms from this angle, but when they take her body to the mortuary they'll notice the scars on her arms and at the top of her thighs. They are so deep the skin looks like corrugated card.

Not long now – there's only a few breaths left in that body. Don't fidget, there's still plenty of time to get to the coffee shop. See, look. That's the fourth person in the last hour that's spat at her. It makes you wonder doesn't it, who stops to take the effort to spit at someone who is dying in a doorway. You'll probably argue that they don't know she's dying, if they did they would try to help her.

Really?

You're watching her die right now.

You can count her last breaths on the fingers of one hand.

What are you doing?

Field Holler

Jim Carruth

Today I stand
in a field and shout.
It is good to stand in a field and shout
to stand somewhere
you can call your own
somewhere you can find a place
  somewhere you can find a space
    somewhere you can call home
                                        and shout

Today I stand up
in my field and shout
and others will stand up
in their fields and shout
I am not alone
in wanting a place called home
I can stand in and shout
  I shout for some cannot hear
    I shout for some will not listen
      I stand up and shout
because each voice is important
      each must be heard,
        each given a chance
          to stand up and shout
in their own language
          their own voice,
                their own field.

Fence and hedge will not keep out
forever
those who do not want you

to stand up and shout
only want you to sing their song
so will come in,
take your shout
take your field

I will not yield to them
but add each lost voice to mine.
Today, in my small field
I stand up and shout.

Home

An extract from the novel Deadly Code

Lin Anderson

The voices were there again. Chitter chatter, chitter chatter. The two men were bad enough, whispering confidences, offering advice. She could just about cope with them.

But not the woman. It was the woman's voice she hated most. Screeching away at her.

Esther's stupid. Esther's stupid.

The wind met her abruptly at the Underground entrance, snatching the voice from her head. She imagined the woman being dragged away screaming, and smiled.

'It's one pound forty.' She was startled back into reality.

'Sorry. Right.'

Her right hand shook as she tried to pluck the ticket from the curved metal tray. The guy waited, his chin raised in mock patience, as she fumbled.

Her hands didn't work any more. They didn't do what she told them.

She walked stiffly to the turnstile. As she presented the ticket, the woman's voice was back, nipping her brain. When the train emerged from the tunnel, the roar momentarily drowned the voice. She looked down at the track and imagined being enveloped in a thick black silence.

Then the woman was back, calling her *a stupid bitch, a stupid fucking bitch.*

Esther stumbled forward, tipping her centre of gravity towards the edge.

Spike was out the door before the girl serving knew he had ever been in. Two boys waiting for hot pies saw him pocket the packet of potato scones from the counter but said nothing.

Spike didn't run. Outside the baker's, the street was busy with school kids eating fast food and dropping the papers at their feet. Spike joined them for a bit, then strolled across the road. No point in being about when the bell went for the end of lunchtime. Folk might wonder why he wasn't back in school with the rest of them. He resisted the warm smell of potato coming from his pocket even though he was hungry. He had plans for the tattie scones.

When he reached the tenement block, he walked straight past the front entrance and nipped in through the back railings in case the woman on the first floor spotted him. He ducked under half-a-dozen grey nappies flapping on a line. Nothing there worth nicking.

When he reached the third floor, he heard the peevish whine of the baby. He didn't like hearing it cry. It reminded him of his wee brother Calum. Next door was flapping open, caught in the stair's sucking breeze. The baby's whine was louder now. 'Christ. Pick it up. Pick the kid up.'

He ignored the bad smell that drifted out the neighbours' door and turned the key in his own. He was halfway in when the baby emitted a high-pitched cry. It was no use. He would have to make sure it was alright. He almost gagged at the smell of stale piss as he made his way to the living room. The baby had stopped whining now and was weeping, a lost sound that expected no answer. Spike pushed open the living room door. It ground its way over broken glass.

He looked about angrily. Where the fuck was she this time? She was on the settee, junked out of her mind. And beside her, head slumped back, mouth hanging open, was the kid's father. Spike swept the baby up from the floor and took it to the bathroom.

He ran the dirty wee hand under the tap and dried it on his shirt. The cut was only a nick, and couldn't have hurt much - it had probably been more shock than pain that had brought on the crying. Spike brushed at the knees of his dirty trousers, sending fragments of glass down the toilet pan.

'Okay. Now what do we do?' he asked his patient.

Some snot escaped the child's nose, ran down his face and met the remains of a tear. Spike pulled a bit of toilet paper off the roll and wiped the mess away.

'Come on,' he said. 'We're leaving.'

He was sharing his dinner with his new best friend when he heard the front door open. He had fried the tattie scones and heated some beans. The baby was sitting surrounded by cushions, wee hands waving in the air in anticipation of the next mashed spoonful. Spike shovelled another one in and handed it a mug of milk. He looked up as Esther came into the kitchen.

'We've got a visitor,' he said.

'So I see.'

She tried to smile, but he knew by the shadows round her eyes.

'It's bad, isn't it?' he said.

'No!'

He jumped at the sharpness of her tone and she looked sorry.

'It's okay. Honestly. It was bad in the Underground but it's quieter now.'

'I made some food,' he said. 'Yours is in the grill.'

They were drinking mugs of tea when the baby's mother banged on the door.

'Did you take the wean?'

'What do you care?'

'Fucking wee smart arse.'

She pushed past Spike and pulled the child up by his arm. He let out a squeal of rage as the biscuit he was eating flew to the floor.

'Don't feed my wean. I've told you before.'

'You feed it then.'

She kicked the door as she went out.

Esther was pale and frightened.

'They were both out of their minds on the settee,' he explained. 'The place smelt like a pisshole.'

Esther looked worried. 'She'll tell the social about you. She knows you're a runaway.'

'Then we'll move,' he said. 'I'm fed up listening to them shagging anyway.'

'Spike.'

'What?'

He could feel his face shift into worry.

'You might not be able to stay here any more.'

'You want me out?'

'No.' She shook her head. 'It's just... if the singing doesn't work out... there won't be any money.'

'There's none now.'

He fetched the pot and poured more tea. He felt fourteen going on forty.

Esther took the mug and nursed it, her mind somewhere else.

Spike wondered about going to a doctor, asking about the voices. When he'd tried to persuade Esther to make an appointment, she'd looked so frightened. He couldn't bear it when she looked at him like that.

'Spike?' She smiled. 'Thanks.'

'What for?'

She leaned forward and touched his head with her lips. 'For everything.' She got up. 'I'd better get ready. Don't want to be late.'

'I'll walk you down.'

She looked as if she might argue, then thought better of it. While she got ready he cleared the dishes and washed up. In his whole life, this was the first place he had been happy. Esther made him happy.

'Right. How do I look?'

She'd changed and put up her hair, revealing the heart-shaped mole. Her eyes were black-rimmed, lashes thick with mascara. She stretched her red mouth into a smile. 'For the punters, right?'

He prayed that the voices would leave her alone for tonight. 'Right,' he said. 'Let's go.'

He liked walking with her. In the dark she could be his girlfriend. In the dark he wasn't fourteen. She put her arm through his. The streets were filling up with punters, blokes set on a night out.

They passed the Fantasy Bar. Four guys got out of a taxi and hung about the steps before they went in. Spike hated them, hated the way they were men before they were human.

'Hey, I'm not there yet,' she said, tugging him on.

The jazz club was busy, a trail of people edging its way in the door.

'I'll see you later,' she said and squeezed his arm.

'I could come in.'

The doorman gave him a look that suggested otherwise.

'I'll be back for you.'

Esther nodded, trying to hide her nervousness.

After she disappeared Spike stood for a while, ignoring the doorman's bugger-off look.

He tried to imagine Esther on stage, the red lips trembling with sound. He thought about looking for a back entrance, finding a way in, hiding, watching her sing.

The doorman had had enough.

'Get lost, son.'

Spike gave him the finger and walked on.

Things were quiet now. He could tell by her eyes. Spike took Esther's hand and slipped it through his arm.

'Chips?'

'Yeah.' She waved the money Sean had given her. 'Let's make it a fish supper.'

The all-night cafe was empty apart from a few stragglers who needed the sustenance in order to get home.

She sat down and handed him the plastic menu with a flourish. 'No expense spared.'

After the feast he said, 'You were great.'

When she asked how he knew, he told her he'd climbed in a toilet window.

She laughed. 'Did anyone see you?'

She laughed even more when he said, 'Only the guy wanking off in the cubicle I landed in. And he wasn't going to tell anybody.'

'And I thought I was singing in a respectable jazz club.'

'Wanking is respectable,' he told her, 'unless you've been brought up…' he came to a halt, a shadow crossing his face.

She reached out and took his hand. 'Like you?'

'Like me.' He went quiet.

'Heh?' She squeezed his hand. 'We're doing fine.'

She was always positive when the voices weren't there. He suspected something in her past had made her ill like this but Esther never spoke about it and he didn't ask. He didn't want to talk about his past either.

They had met in Tesco's. She was shopping, he was there to steal something to eat. She spotted him slipping a tin of corned beef in his pocket and made him put it in her trolley. When they got to the counter, she paid for it.

Outside she asked him where he was staying and he took too long to lie, so she took him home. In his head he made her the big sister he never had. It didn't always work.

'Okay,' she said. 'Let's go home.'

Spike stood up, happy. He loved it when she spoke like that, as if they would be together forever. He had played out the scenario a million times in his head. It didn't matter that he was only fourteen. He could look after Esther, hold her when she was frightened, even maybe…

He shut down his brain at that point. He hated himself for even thinking about making a move on her. He would never do that. Never.

Her voice punctured his thoughts.

'Sean was great. Even when I almost blew it in the toilet.'

'What?'

'Someone came in when… when things were bad. She told Sean I was taking stuff.'

'Jesus.'

She smiled at his worried face. 'It's okay. I told him I had a migraine and was sick. He believed me.'

He hated when the voices came and he wasn't with her. Sometimes he felt they were waiting for him to go away, just so they could torment her.

They were passing a block of red sandstone tenements. On the ground floor, plants filled a window box and trailed down in a burst of flowers. Their scent hung heavy in the night air.

'Maybe we could move,' she said suddenly, 'get a better flat.'

She grabbed his arm in excitement. 'Sean says he can run me six weeks, maybe more. With that sort of money I could put down a deposit on a decent place. Sean says once the word is out I'll get more gigs.'

Spike fought back the fear that slid up his throat. Now she was back singing, she might not need him any more.

She touched his arm. 'You'll come with me, won't you Spike?' Her voice was small and lonely again.

His fear subsided.

'Of course I will.'

Then he thought about the baby.

'We'll tell the social about the baby,' she said, reading his mind.

The child was half-starved. It would be totally starved if Spike wasn't there to feed it.

'She was going to shop you anyway.'

Esther was right. The mother was always threatening to tell the authorities about him. It was only a matter of time. And the baby wasn't his responsibility.

'Okay.' He tried a smile. 'Okay.'

She was happy now. They had a plan, a plan for the future.

Above them, the street lamps sent soft lights to reflect their images in the puddles. Spike saw them there together, arm in arm.

Nothing or nobody would get them, he decided. He would see to that.

When they reached the tenement block, the stairwell was in darkness. He took her hand and they negotiated the broken bottles that littered the entrance. He felt in his pocket for his lighter.

'Some bastard's smashed the lights.'

He went up the left hand side, sliding his arm along the wall, encouraging the small blue flame to light up the next step.

When they reached their landing, Spike produced the key.

'Spike.' Esther pointed at the broken lock.

'What the fuck!'

He made a move to go in, but she caught his arm.

'No.' Her face was terrified in the flare of the lighter.

Whoever was inside had heard them. Footsteps came towards the door. Esther ran for the stairs. Spike flipped the lighter shut and followed. They stumbled their way down. They were one level below when they heard the door open. Spike held Esther against him. He could feel the thump of her heart.

'There's nobody there,' a man's voice called.

Esther gave a whimper. As the door swung shut, Spike took a quick look. A thickset figure was framed in the doorway.

Esther's eyes were wide with fear.

'Who was it?'

She was shaking, her words rattling through her teeth. Spike suddenly realised she thought the intruder had come looking for her.

'We have to get away from here,' she pleaded.

He took off his jacket and put it round her. 'It's okay. I think it was the Flintstone guy from next door,' he lied. 'He probably came to give me a kicking for taking the baby again.'

Relief flooded her face. 'Are you sure?'

He nodded. 'We'll come back tomorrow. He'll have given up by then.'

Spike ran it over in his mind. His own fear of discovery had started just after he met Esther. Bags, the Big Issue seller, had shown him a photo. It didn't look like him and even Bags didn't recognise him from it. In the photo his hair was short and neat.

'Looks like a computer nerd,' Spike had said, trying to sound casual. 'Who's looking for him?'

'A Yank. Gave me a twenty to keep a lookout.'

'Easy shit.'

'Yeah. Wish he was looking for me.'

Bags had a phone number to call. He waved it in front of Spike like another twenty.

'So if you see the nerd?'

'Sure.'

If an American was looking for him, it had to be something to do with his father. A cold knot formed in Spike's chest.

He'd been even more careful after that. If it hadn't been for Esther he would have left Glasgow, gone to London. They would never find him there.

They bedded down in the park under a tree, Esther curled against him, he holding his body a celibate inch away. Eventually she slept and he listened to the soft sound of her breathing.

She had told him once that the voices were there in her sleep, weaving their way into her dreams. He imagined people attached to these disembodied voices and routinely killed them to set her free, but they always came back to haunt her, especially when she was nervous or frightened.

The voices were sent to punish her. That's what she believed. Punish her for what?

Spike had no idea who the guy in their flat had been, but it wasn't their neighbour. He had been convinced it was somebody looking for him, but Esther thought the man had come for her and it had frightened the wits out of her.

Who was Esther afraid of? Some old boyfriend who'd been bad to her? Spike hated the thought of someone hurting Esther. He hated the thought of someone else being with her.

Spike felt his cock harden and immediately pulled back from the warmth of Esther's body.

He spat his distaste for himself into the grass.

'Heh.' She was awake and watching.

He jumped up and walked towards the bushes, afraid she would see his erection.

When he re-emerged, she was ready to go.

They went back to the cafe.

Esther was listless and Spike sensed she had entered that other world. The world of voices that told her she was shite, a nothing who didn't deserve to live.

'Esther?'

She didn't respond.

'Esther! Look at me.'

She lifted her head.

'We'll find somewhere else to stay. I promise.'

Escaping the Rat Race

Noel Kempster

1) Escaping the Rat Race

In the 1960s we saw the Hippies. Anything and everything was possible. All you need is love! This zeitgeist, this sense of liberation and escape from the conventions of the period was a precursor for the notion which underpinned the TV program *The Good Life*. To many *The Good Life* was a light-hearted comedy program but to me and like-minded dreamers *The Good Life* was an invitation to escape the Rat Race. At the same time John Seymour wrote a manual describing how this could be done. Was this a bizarre, even dangerous notion or a dreamer's paradise?

Well my milking cows in Wiltshire using a moveable bale in an open field where there was no concrete and at a time of very low milk prices, so low the government paid a 5d per gallon subsidy, was going nowhere. So, some would say, in a fit of madness, I sold my house and bought into the dream – a twenty-six acre croft with a But N Ben dwelling in Stronsay called Newfield. The four of us, my wife Meryl, Rebecca my daughter who was twelve and my son Timothy eleven upped sticks and went to Stronsay an island with a population of 230 divided between those that went to church and those that went to the pub. Stronsay, is a flat windswept piece of land measuring seven miles by seven miles and is two hours sail from the Orkney mainland. There was little else other than a church and a pub. Oh there was a primary school but Bec and Tim were now secondary school age and they had to go to Kirkwall Grammar School and reside in the school hostel. Our family of four became a family of two – for ever. Twenty-eight years later I still carry a painful image in my head of Bec's stubborn face as she turned away from us in the street and headed for her new school and hostel. Before going to Orkney Tim showed signs of being dyslexic, a disorder not universally accepted at that time. On one occasion Tim became so frustrated with English and French that he threw his books out of the classroom window. We were concerned and contacted the school about the issue. As a result we had a visit from the educational psychologist. He assured us that Tim would be fine. Tim was very bright with computers and chess which caused older pupils to bully him and computers were the future. Tim now has PhD in computer science and at his graduation ceremony took prize after prize. His tutor took Meryl and I out to dinner. Bec is now a teacher in Yorkshire and speaks Japanese and Chinese. Yes, schooling was first class but the loss to the family during their secondary school years is profoundly regrettable.

2) Homeless

On arrival in Stronsay I needed to focus making the But N Ben dwelling into a home to live in which was a major investment of money and my time. The bank took a charge on the croft and lent me money at the eye-watering rate of 15% per annum. *The Good Life* and Mr Seymour's book were remiss on this detail. I had a bank loan but my first impulse was to conserve cash and to this end teamed up with another island incomer, Russell, to leave the island and get a well-paid job in the oil industry. The centre of the oil industry is Aberdeen. So leaving Meryl to fend for herself in a second-hand caravan, we left the island and became homeless and with very little money. We boarded a small ferry for the two hour sail to Scrabster and a larger ferry to cross the Pentland Firth from Scrabster to Caithness on the Scottish mainland. On a freezing cold night just before Christmas we found ourselves in an Aberdeen hostel. We had a roof over our heads and were out of the cold. However the hostel had a pervasive sickly smell that seemed to settle on my stomach. As it was past mealtime when we arrived I remember that we were given some small cakes. These also carried the same sickly smell as the hostel and I could not swallow a bite.

To sleep I lay on a wooden plank in a small cubicle but lay awake the whole night hearing pitiful moans and ceaseless coughing. I could understand why rough sleepers preferred to lay sleeping bags on cardboard in street doorways to sleep on. However I have since learnt that this has its dangers and have witnessed a rough doorway sleeper being woken up by the police and when she ran for it was caught, handcuffed and put in a police van. I could not understand why the police left the spot without lifting a man who slept beside the girl. As it turned out Jane also had a police issue.

Back at the hostel morning came and with it the morning optimism. Russell and I pressed on, seeking potential employers in the oil industry. But we were woefully ill-prepared, having no well-scripted CV, no experience in the oil industry and no contacts to introduce us to labouring jobs. We found no openings. On our third day in Aberdeen homeless and forlorn we were scooped up by a Salvation Army officer who took us to a small private hotel where we were given a meal and slept in a comfortable bed. What a Christmas present that was! We came to the conclusion that we were not going to find well-paid work in the oil industry and with low-paid work we were no better off than being in Stronsay. Russell continued south and I returned to the croft. Russell and I were homeless for a very short period and we did not have to come to terms with the curfews nor part of the warehousing of homeless people in a system that becomes endless as is the case in some hostels today.

3) The Land

Back in Stronsay I ran two different projects. One self-sufficient proper, the other was an attempt to build a viable commercial business shepherding sheep and keeping hens to produce free range eggs. A small acreage would house a lot of free range hens. With profits I could build a home. In the self-sufficiency project I reared two calves and sold them as breeding heifers. Being in small numbers and given individual attention they grew well, even became pets. These cows must have had a rude awaking when they joined a commercial herd. The pigs were more difficult to control and once when being transported at marketing size they squeezed through six inch nets and we had the whole island looking for them. Hens were sold in small numbers to other islands. They were transported squeezed into small crates I made. Given space they would cannibalise each other and I stood the danger of a criminal prosecution for cruelty to animals.

With a small rowing boat I bought, Russell, who had returned to the island, and I set out fishing to catch fish and lobsters. There was a market for lobsters on the island. However, lobsters were over-fished and the odd one we caught was small and should have been thrown back in the sea to grow, but Russell took them home and boiled them. I learned how to make lobster pots and Russell knew how to catch fish using a line and hooks. Those fish that were not infected with parasitic worms Russell's wife filleted and we shared out the catch. I milked Daisy the goat every day for our milk. We tried eating limpets we prized from the rocks but found they were as tough as rubber no matter how long we boiled them. On our own Meryl and I could have lived a self-sufficient lifestyle, although Meryl and the kids have never forgiven me for subjecting them to its constraints. Digging a hole in a field as a toilet and filling it and carrying water five hundred yards etc was too much and Meryl and the kids living away from home was too much and I have never been forgiven for subjecting them to it.

I was tempted to go ahead with the commercial projects by the generous government grants, both agricultural grants and house improvement grants. I fenced the two fields, borrowed a tractor and reseeded the fields and even drained the larger field using only grant money. I then overstocked with a flock of sheep that included four seaweed-eating North Ronaldsay sheep to keep the genetic pool going. I hoped to be able to rent more land to get through the winter but I hadn't been on the island long enough and this didn't happen. I resorted to feeding the sheep silage on which they did not thrive and a lot of lambs were born dead. Also I arranged to house the sheep in a cosy neighbour's barn and the sheep promptly began to die from stress. I put them back in the field. I lost more lambs when at a very young age they had their eyes picked were picked out by black backed seagulls. A neighbour offered to guard the lambs with his gun but the gulls simply waited until he was not there. A neighbour let me run the remaining thirty lambs in fields he did not use until they were collected and shipped to France. The buyer of the lambs remarked how well the drainage in my field was working. My own grass grew well with the use of ample hen muck and I grew a bumper crop of hay. This I had to give away as payment for the silage delivered the previous winter. At that time free range eggs sold at a premium in Glasgow. I built a professionally designed laying house to stand up to the strong winds, stocked with 5000 laying hens reared from day old chicks that were flown in... One night as pullets a large number decided to crowd into one rearing house leaving me to meet a pile of dead pullets the next morning. I was getting the hang of burying dead animals. Glasgow was too far away to cover the cost of shipping eggs from Stronsay and I lost money.

There were good grants to build a cesspit and to put plumbing into the house. Also I hired a building firm from Westray to do much of the skilled work in the house. I think that they ripped me off. I laid a concrete floor with Russell's help. I built the house only to have it taken away from me by the bank. I bet the farm to build a house we could live in – and lost.

Anne Sears, John Seymour's daughter, has said, 'I have met people who said my father ruined them.'

Depressing

February 24th, 1997

Jacqui Cathcart

Can't go on I'm all puffed out
What the fuck's life all about
Things going wrong all the time
Nothing good in this world of mine.

So much sadness, hurt, and pain
Stress and worry it's all the same
When did I last feel okay and well
Is it three or six years I just can't tell.

Been down so long, just can't cope no way
Using lots of effort to just get through the day
That might sound daft but not to me
'Cos my dreams are better than reality.

I couldn't feel worse even if I tried
So cold and numb I'm just empty inside
With a great big hole that's inside of me
I feel so lonely I wish I was free.

It seems like forever I've felt so low
When will this pain and heartache go
It hurts so much now I always cry
How much longer and please tell me why???

When will it be over I can't say when
Could be soon or ages till I'm happy again
Been down so long depressed and sad
Wish I was dead I feel so bad…

Domestic Abuse

Jacqui Cathcart

Trapped in a relationship, feeling so low
No one to turn to, nowhere to go
You can't do this, you can't do that
And if do, you'll get a slap.

Cut off from your family and friends
When does it stop, where does it end
Years of abuse, doing what you're told
But you cannot leave, you're not that bold.

It's so different now to when you first met
There's so, so much that you regret
Wish you'd listened to what people said
Maybe you would just be better off dead.

He's chipped away at the person you were
Pretending all along he really does care
Took away all your confidence, self esteem too
Would he really do that if he loved you?

He manipulates you, he's really good
Doesn't treat you the way he should
When did it all go so very wrong?
You used to be happy and really strong.

An abusive man is the worst kind
Physically or playing with your mind
But it's hard to leave, start anew
So you stay and allow him to mistreat you.

Now you cry a silent cry at night
Haven't even got the strength to fight
Carry on as if it's all fine too
Letting no one know what you're going through.

The Chip Roll

David Pettigrew

The pan was on the hob, the lard ready to spit. He was just about to put in the chips when there she was, staring through the window. He paused, bowl in hand, sizing up the disapproval on her face. He'd hung the washing on the pulley half an hour ago and she hated him frying when clothes were hung up. Especially chips because they stank the place out. Take the washing down, her look was saying, STOP MAKING A MESS. He looked at the cooker, then back at the window. She'd gone.He dropped the chips in the pan. The sound was like a round of applause.

It was a week since he'd seen her, but he was breaking kitchen rules so he wasn't surprised. Obviously it had been a trick of the light – it was November and dreich outside and he'd just put on the strip light so his eyes were adjusting. But it was funny to think she'd come back to give him a row. Upstairs he heard a door slam and he paused again, then gave a wee laugh. It'd be just like her to storm off in a huff. He stirred the chips with the slotted spoon and breathed in the steam. Cooking like this drove her up the wall, turning the place into a chip shop. In fact, it had been verboten towards the end. His daughter had put a stop to it.

'Dad, you know she doesn't like it. It's really hard for Mum, you just carrying on, doing your thing, while she's…' Vivien's face had creased up so he had no alternative but to slide the chips he'd just cut into the bin. 'There, there Viv,' he'd said, giving her a wee pat. 'It'll be all right.' But she'd flinched at his touch. 'You don't get it, do you Dad? It's not going to be all right.' She wiped away a tear with her wrist. 'We talked about this yesterday. But you've forgotten already.' At that point, he'd stared down at his slippers, attempting the dewy eyed look for himself. It seemed to work. 'Dad, you're doing a lot of that lately. Forgetting things. You left your keys in the front door the other day. Anyone could've come in. I know it's hard, the stress. Why don't you go and see Doctor Liddell?'

Given what'd been happening upstairs, Liddell was clearly an arse who couldn't diagnose an advanced case of the bubonic plague. But he had nodded and kissed his daughter's cheek. He'd go to the Chip Chick Inn later when he went for his walk. It never happened. Just as he reached the door of the chip shop, the mobile in his anorak had started to buzz. Right to the last, his wife got her way.

With the chips sizzling nicely, he opened the wall cupboard to get his favourite mug, the big one with *Glasgow's Miles Better* on it. The mug cupboard was actually the lower one, under the countertop, while the upper one stored the tinned stuff, beans and custard and pineapple slices. But it was handy up there, right above the kettle. He stepped back, confused. The mug wasn't there. He checked the cupboard next it to it – not there either. Suddenly anxious, he opened the door under the counter top, and there it was, in with the other mugs and glasses. He shook his head as he threw in a teabag. Maybe she had come back. The mug was old and chipped but the size made a cup of tea last longer and he always said the wee smiley face in the picture cheered him up. She said it was an eyesore. It'd be just like her to put it out the way. Everything had to be just so.

'Bloody woman,' he said as he buttered a roll. But maybe Vivien was right. Maybe his memory was going. He'd noticed a few things, especially in the last week. The keys in the door, the light left on in the bathroom after he was sure he'd turned it off. He pushed the thought away. Let it be his wife. She'd spent her life being a control freak – why change now?

The chips were golden, so he scooped them into the colander with the slotted spoon and held it over the sink for the lard to drain out. She always had a meltdown when he did that, as the lard solidified quickly on the stainless steel, making it hard to wipe off. He'd shown her the trick of pouring boiling water over it from the kettle, but all he'd got was a load of moaning about the u-bend clogging up. Daft cow, she'd even fuss about stuff she couldn't see – he'd told her that the last time she caught him.

'One of these days I'm going to murder you,' was the reply.

He shook the colander and set it down, lard leaking over the counter top. It was nearly time for his programme. He could tidy up later. Maybe Viv could do it when she popped in at teatime.

Quickly he poured the kettle into the mug and loaded the roll with some chips, piling the rest over the plate. From the living room he could hear the theme tune booming from the telly so he got to work with the salt, splashed the vinegar and decided the sauce could wait till he was parked in the armchair. He picked up the mug and the bottle of sauce with one hand, and carried the plate with the other. Using his foot, he hooked open the door, then used it again to pull it shut as he stepped into the hall. It was a bit dark in there so he pushed the light on with his nose. There was another switch at the living room end and when he nosed that one off he saw the kitchen light shining from the gap under the door. Wasting electricity was the thing that really sent her mental and the habit of turning off lights was ingrained. But the theme tune was finishing and it was too late to go back. Actually he didn't need to go back. The applause started – he was just in time.

He'd turned the gas fire on earlier and the room was lovely and toasty. He set the things on the side table and sank down in the chair. Afternoons in front of the fire were brilliant, especially since she'd taken to her bed. The room was his – he could watch the football he'd taped or the afternoon western, anything instead of bloody *Bargain Hunt*. And he could have it turned up as high as he liked.

Countdown was his favourite, mainly for the cracking wee blonde who did the sums. Settling back, he rested the plate on his lap and opened the roll. He unscrewed the sauce bottle and shook it gently, watching the sauce land in red dollops over the chips.

He lifted the roll to his mouth and was about to bite when he remembered the chip pan. Did he turn it off? He couldn't remember. On countdown a conundrum had started but it couldn't wait. He put the roll down and moved the plate back on the table and was about to push himself out of the chair, when he heard it. A knock from above. Or was it the tick-tock from Countdown? He fumbled for the remote and turned the telly down a bit. There it was again. Definitely a knock, coming from the bedroom. When she'd got really bad he'd started sleeping on the settee, and they had a system that she'd knock on the bedside table if she needed him. Usually it was just enough for him to hear through the ceiling, but sometimes – when he felt like it – he didn't.

Knock.

Knock.

But all that was done with a week ago.

Knock.

For Christ's sake, don't be daft.

He stood up. He'd heard the bedroom door slam earlier so he must've left the window open. The draught would be coming in and knocking something over. In the hall, he switched on the light and went up the stairs. The bedroom door was shut – he shoved it open and went inside. Everything was as they'd left it. The bedclothes were stripped, the duvet folded at the foot of the mattress. She'd been on a drip because she couldn't swallow, but they'd forgotten the stand. He'd get Viv to take it away when she popped in later.

He shivered. The window was open and knocking in the wind – the stay had come loose. He walked across and righted it, leaving the window open. After they'd taken her away it had been pretty smelly in here; he wanted to make sure it was gone.

From downstairs he heard the tick-tock of another conundrum and he remembered his roll. It'd be getting cold and he didn't want to waste homemade chips. He shut the door and hurried back down the stairs and along the hall. It was much warmer down here, really cosy. He'd just stay on the settee. Back in the living room he settled into the chair and turned up the telly.

The wee blonde was doing the sums and the chips smelled great. He wolfed down the roll and then savoured the chips on the plate, one by one. King Edwards – fluffy, flavoursome, soaked in vinegar and sauce.

With the last chip and the last mouthful of tea, he was full. The gas fire hissed and the tick-tock of another conundrum made his eyelids droop. What was it he was to do again? He'd forgot. Och, he'd see to it later, whatever it was. Or Viv could do it when she popped in at teatime. He laid his hands over his belly. A wee nap just now, he thought. This is the life.

In the hall, smoke poured through the gap under the door.

Safe Home

Katy Hastie

At its highest point, the cliff-face of An Sgurr is so steep you can't see it when you reach it and look down. An inch from the edge felt like my next step would land me straight onto the land below, smooth as a blanket thrown over the rolls of burnished bracken, shining paths and flattened grass. It looked like the island of Eigg was waiting to catch me. Maybe two steps more and I would have made it to Eigg's new harbour and wet my toes in the puddle of the bay. Between the smallness of the land below me and the largeness of my soggy trainers on the volcanic rock, it was tempting to believe myself a giantess. I did feel the tallest thing around for miles. To the north the sharp-iced Cullins were shoulder height. To the east, over an arms-length of glinting sea, the mainland horizon cracked into yellow glens and white-capped mountains. Was it any wonder the iron-age inhabitants built a fort here? Who would be mad enough to invade from the coast if they saw that? I wanted to be as bold and strong as the legendary tall women warriors that walked into the still Loch nam Ban Mora behind me. I felt the lightness that comes when a lift stops, or a wave crests, then a dangerous sense of scale sunk in and I wished for myself to get home safe. I wished for no wind to strike up and throw me off the rock, no crumbling path to trip me up, no rain to freeze me. I wished to make it back down in one piece. And in that, the wish was granted.

It was the little walking guide in my pocket that told me if I made it to the top of the An Sgurr I should make a wish. The paper had become crumpled with my repeated attempts to follow the path but I was grateful for it. I was grateful too for the sunshine drying my socks. And I was grateful for the orange dots sprayed to the rocks to direct back from the soggy wrong turns that caused them. The dots had taken me into the shadow side of the mound, across the watery bogs, up the pale moss-coloured boulders and through the fanned sides of an ancient dry-stone wall that marks the entry point to the top. The way up was simple once you found it. It was harder to navigate once you were up there amongst the hardened volcanic bubbles. One grey rockery looks much like another and you can't cut a path through stone. There wasn't even enough mud or grass to indent a footprint to find later. Again, the orange dots kept me right. I'm not sure I would have found the safe ways to scramble to the peak without them. Trusting the orange dots got me to the top and on the way down, I found them on the reverse side of the same rocks. With no-one else around, this small sign of another person looking out for me, thinking of my safety and my freedom, felt like human warmth and I made a point to touch each one.

For all our apparent boundless courage as a species, all of us, at some point, feel the same wish. Often I'll say it to friends before we leave each other for the night – get home safe. But working with writers for whom home is not necessarily a place of safety, it made me question what makes us feel like we have made it 'home'. What makes us belong to a place, or think a place feels anything for us? Nationhood as an ideal often looks for safety in ethnicity, religion, gender roles, borders, colonies, empire. Control. But the earth below us is rarely so stable, our DNA that obedient, our childhoods that reassuring, our societies that collective and our minds so willing. The uncertainty makes the project all the more desperate, all the more critical, all the more violent and unjust.

The incoherence of belonging is something every child is schooled into forgetting. That day you realise the difference of your playmates matters. In a way I'm grateful for learning this young. A thumping brass band to me will always be the sound of a boundary being bashed into place between either sides of my family. What you think of as home can be hostile but it is still your home if it was where you are loved. When you know your loved ones, finances and freedoms can be pulled up like floorboards, such confidence must feel misplaced. And maybe rightfully so, from the very beginning, from each of our conceptions, safety and home is a moveable concept inside the bodies of our mothers, a transitional place of growth we will always outgrow and venture outwards from. One day, the waters will break and we will be on our own. Some of us know this better than others.

Eigg is an island off the North West coast of Scotland. I went there on my own to find out more about their legends and the way they carry a trace of a matriarchal pre-Christian culture in a story they tell, about their tall women warriors. One Easter Sunday, the big women, angry at incoming Christian missionaries, come to kill Saint Donnan and all his monks as they gather for mass in their newly built monastery. The big women warriors agree to let the holy men celebrate mass and enjoy their Easter feast, then put them all to the sword. That night, bright lights rise from the monk's heaped bodies and lure the big women into a deep loch behind An Sgurr. Usually they are tall enough to leap over the stones and cross the water, but this time they are too entranced to find their footing and they drown. The big women exit, pursuing lights. The water becomes Loch nam Ban Mora, the loch of the big women. A story to account for a sudden population upheaval, perhaps. The women disappear into the landscape to make way for the men to rule the land. The first part of making a place home may be telling a story about it, but this act of creative invention, or destruction, never fully averts the past, even as it tries to build a future.

To each of us is charged the task of making ourselves 'at home', but what if you never had it in the first place? Or it was taken from you? Our society tends to tell us a story about winners and losers, making it appear inevitable that some will make it and some not, sacrifice necessary, worth monetary, help too hard, history too tangled to find justice, lives too broken to fix. Unless you've lived this story or listened closely to someone who has, it's hard to understand how inadequate it is, how stepping outside it opens a multitude of other stories, how creative the act of survival is – how generous the act of sharing that experience is, to show edges that we barely see, far less cross.

This project's writers gave me a story to read about a newly arrived asylum seeker called Baj and his attempts to find a place to live. I was curious about how the writer's experience of migration would inform the story but the story of Baj was like nothing I'd ever read before. The story began with Baj's case-workers, kind Saj and stern Maj. They tell Baj he has to take up a housing offer from the ominous 'offering association' but he only has one shot to make a bid for the flat he wants. Feeling the pressure of others putting in notes of interest and bidding, he risks his one offer all on a place he later finds out is substandard, badly located and beyond his price range. With help from his friend Raj he manages to navigate a maze of different organisations and people to get help, each one with spookily similar names: Laj, Caj and Daj in the town of (you've guessed it) Naj. The parable put me squarely in Baj's shoes: desperately trying to find a home using an unintelligible language that all sounds the same and the mystifying bureaucracy of another culture. It also gave me a profound lesson in change, in being a human being. What is it you retain when you reconstitute your personality to survive in a hostile society? For the writer, it was his dead-pan satirical sense of humour against authority. The press would read this story as exactly the type of resource-grabbing free-for-all they salivate over. But to adapt this hard, to be 'at home' after trauma and on your own, is less a kind of 'getting home safely' and more a hopeful free-fall for survival. Home is a place you are welcomed and contribute to, it is always changed by your presence, and perhaps it needs you to change it. Stories can be one way to make room.

'Home' is not necessarily a place of safety. Far too often the home hearth acts as the ideological battlefront of 'normality', 'goodness' and 'health', but maybe that's because the battle lines were already scored across the living-room carpet between cohesion and individuation, coagulating homogeny and rebellious freedom. At its worst, 'home' can be a shaky edifice, reliant on the collusion and corrosion of the inhabitants to keep secrets safe, damage unreleased, keep calm and carry on. But truth will out. Somehow it always finds a crack, an opening, somewhere, sometime, to demand a hearing, even if it breaks the carrier in the process. Words may or may not be one of the safer forms it takes, much depends on the listener and the help given. We are the stories we tell ourselves, even when we are not telling them yet. We are the stories we tell other people, even when, and maybe especially when, they can see through them.

A question I came to consider in this project: when should a writer use 'I'? Some writers found safe distance in using 'he' or 'she' or 'you'. Some found themselves more exposed in that hiding place, or doubted they could take on such airs. Some opted to own their 'I'. Others created characters. Traumatic experience does not deny someone the right to creative autonomy and craftsmanship in how they tell a story. You have a right to as much distance or disclosure of your life as you decide, and only you know, or don't know. These creative boundaries are porous and unknowable, even to the writer. When you write, the teller of the story is absent in person but so present in the reader's imagination that sometimes reading your own words yields surprises. Who are they, where are they, when? Did this really happen? Is it the truth? Is it really you? Is this me? These are the foundations of how we talk to each other and how stories are believed. Writing builds a 'home' for your words, you create a space from which to speak every bit as much as what you say. This is both liberating and terrifying. It replays our own journeys from the homes we've had to the homes we've made, or failed to, or the homes we've been ejected from. It indulges fantasies of what we'd like to be and what we are scared we are. It is a tentative stepping out on ground you created yourself and can just as easily be pulled away. Sometimes you might want it to be. In completing a story a version of yourself is honoured and discarded. The water breaks, you walk away.

Such reliance on self-reliance makes guidance tricky. It runs the risk of taming the unruly qualities that made writing important. The best I could offer were options, some orange dots round obstacles, but it was more important to encourage than chide, nurture than direct. After all, I was learning as much as they were, if not more. One day I got an email with the title: 'Feed me back'. It puzzled me for a while before I realised a word I use so regularly meant exactly what it said.

What struck me most in hearing stories from those for whom a safe home is or was not a certainty, was a renewed faith that we feel like we exist more when we create. That creative writing, truthfully or fantastically, in every word that hits the page, is a coming home to the self, not in the crude sense of finding the 'real' you, more in the sense of being allowed to be lots of yous, in motion – true story or not. Of wanting to be listened to. Of wanting to listen. Of changing yourself and those around you by saying these words. Of change by exchange. Your story for my attention. My prejudice for your truth. In being allowed to speak, you are allowed to be a person. We make room.

The An Sgurr I made a wish on was once a lake. The guide book told me that during the great volcanic eruptions that left their stems in the Cullins, molten lava rolled into the cold water and solidified, casting its depths forever. As time and glaciers passed, and the softer land eroded, the solid lake upturned into a high peak. The crest of a wave I felt that day was there, every bit as much as I felt the grain of weathered stone on my fingertips or the sunshine on my back or the bog water in my shoes. If the ground we stand on can change, then home has to be something we construct to protect what we can as we go. At our highest points, it's hard to make sense of how easily it falls apart, but equally at our lowest it's hard to see how anyone can get back up. In different ways, each of the writers on this project climbed a hill and made a wish at the top, that you read their story. That you grant them room to be heard with the same motility and resilience they granted their stories during the risky redrafting and editing process to get them to finished forms. But no story really ends, it rebegins with every reader, just as one day, even when An Sgurr is the last surface on Eigg sticking out of the water, stories about it will probably still be passed from person to person.

C'est la vie...

Jamie Jackson

Sitting in the cafe without a drink is such a strange thing to do. It always seemed like a pressure to buy, to consume something, usually tall slim and golden but even a pint of lager seemed strange here. Always a pricey little half thing served up by some grumpy well-groomed waiter.

You'd think with all the sunshine here in Paris it would make the people cheery bit no. The sun seemed to shine through the windows with a hard intensity. Casting hard shadows along the streets, cooking everything in its path.

The smells from last night's rubbish always made the air sour. A kind of fruity pong mixed with diesel always lurched in the air. Hanging about just as he was. Something had to give, it had been three days now and he still hadn't found his metro pass. Sitting here day after day killing time hoping something, anything, would break the monotony of work, eat, sleep.

Oh well another overpriced coffee it is then. David was slim, slimmer than he thought and slimmer than most young men should be at 5'10. He wasn't eating as well as he should. A daily diet of bananas, pasta and carrots wasn't really enough for a twenty five year old lad who's on his feet all day walking an hour and a half on the baking heat along the length of the Seine to Le Champs.

He knew this, but a little social beer or coffee once a week was all he allowed himself. Sitting inside in the sun with a French dictionary just seemed like punishment. Definitely better to get out and see people even if they don't see you. He'd never felt so invisible in his life.

The noise from the street filled the bar, some vaguely familiar French dance pop, tracks blared out the teensy tiny sound system from behind the bar. Nobody at the bar but himself, it still took twenty minutes to get the waiter's attention and longer again to get the drink.

Was it him, was it something he was doing wrong? Tipping his change, was it too little or just not done. Everything and everybody seemed to be against him. It wouldn't be long before he became one of the infamously named poissons morts. You see them on the metro. Great faces sombre staring wide eyes ahead only moving as the train shunted from side to side from station to station. The dead fish faces of the locals. No contact, just existing, barely alive.

Just then the mechanical roar of a motorbike grabbed his attention. Too big to be a moped, he turned to see the hot guy he'd noticed the past week or so dismount his scrambler bike.

Arnaud was a big guy and even from a short distance he looked like a rogue. His black leather biking jacket was taut around the shoulders and his tight jeans bulged with muscles. David guessed that riding a bike must be good exercise. He didn't seem the type to go to the gym. Or even drink and now David's mind turned to the wine he'd spent the last of his week's pay on.

It was so important to get this right, going to someone's house for dinner, especially a French house, more so a French stranger's house. He hoped the wine was good, he was enthusiastically shown the rule of thumb on how to pick a good bottle and name, using your thumb to gauge the quality of the bottle by how far the knuckle of your thumb sinks in from the base.

He was assured it was a good house and good bottle and would pass as table wine. Hoping it wasn't the gin talking he tipped the homeless lad and lassie for their advice. It better be worth the last twenty euros he had. They seemed pleased to be asked and of use and David felt their advice on alcohol and experience would be qualified if nothing else.

Was it wise to spend your last twenty euros and rely on this guy to get you home?

Lost in thought.

Vrrrrrrrooooooooom.

The bloody moped came out of nowhere.

'Look right!' Arnaud was on top of him now, reaching out and sweeping him up onto his feet before he knew it.

'Ça va Daveeeed? Look right, you must always look right, you're not in England anymore.'

Trying to regain his composure and wondering where to put the wine, he was thinking aloud as usual.

'I'm not English, I told you that. I'm from Scotland you know, the best part of England!'

David was feeling pleased he'd regained the situation with humour, satisfied with Arnaud's questioning smile and big brown eyes. He had no idea what he was thinking, no matter. It was all so exciting. He couldn't believe his luck when Arnaud had come over to chat him up the other week when he'd been sat on his own as usual looking through places to rent.

Glad of the distraction and the handsome company David leapt at the chance to make new friends immediately. Dinner with Arnaud and his friends versus another night cramping Fabienne's space.

Between homes and sleeping on her sofa, grateful for her charity but glad of the chance to be out and about, was there a choice?

Arnaud was biking, this was unexpected! How were we to get there?

'Simples just hop on behind me, we will go together.'

'Non, non I will fall off there's only one seat!'

Laughing now.

'It weeeeel be fine.'

Arnaud hops onto the bike which actually seemed a lot bigger up close and dirtier and well just more real somehow. Suddenly this was not something other people do.

How to mount a scrambler and look cool with a bottle of plonk was not on the list.

'Hup.'

'Ok Daveeed.'

'Hold on!!!!!'

The noise was fantastic and to see people stare as the bike roared down the narrow streets as David's legs stiffened holding on tighter than he should but afraid the next turn would be his last.

Heart racing, the Seine was lit all around, bright globes zipped past faster now as they hit full throttle.

'Where are we going?'

'Dinner of course!!!'

'Is it far?'

They were racing along towards Montparnasse and this part of town was different, the streets had grand looking rooftops and ornate window details.

Money?

It looked like money.

David had mixed emotions now, the wine was suddenly seeming to look very, very cheap.

'Debark.'

'Ok we are here – nous et ici.'

David had parked up on a wide street, la tour Montparnasse loomed over the street, ominously unwelcome in the City of Lights. As the night grew cold David braced himself as Arnaud popped in the entry code.

'Wow look at that.'

'What the staircase? Yes we use the lift.'

'Really, it's amazing look at the iron work, it's all art nouveau.' As they entered the lift it slammed shut, making that grating noise. It was tight, too tight, they'd hardly said a word along the way, this was dinner with Arnaud huh? He rides a scrambler and his block is like a palace.

'This way.' They were out the lift and on the sixième étage. The floors were lit with little lights with bluebell-like shades. Beautiful but not giving quite enough light to make out the scale of the interior. The landing reached out into the darkness.

Black and gold the wall opened up in front of them.

Was it even a door?

Stepping from the vault.

'Allo you must be David. I am Victor and these are my friends Step and Michael. So pleased to meet you. Arnaud has told me so much about you.'

Surprised.

'Really, he's a man of few words.'

Smiles all around.

'Pleased to meet you all. I'm terrible with names and sorry my French is poor.'

'Come, come this way we have already the chef and the table is set. The cook assures us that there will be something here we can all enjoy.'

Releasing the bottle of wine apologising that it might be table wine, things look so formal, so expensive, so daunting.

The shrimp stared back at David, expecting a response. The table wine to one side was disregarded but that was to be expected.

The chef was like someone from a magazine. He disappeared after explaining how to eat the doomed crustaceans. This seemed peculiar.

Why didn't he join us? Smiling faces all around and yes a little more wine would be nice.

David was now feeling light headed. The room was blurry and everyone was smiling saying that's OK.

The hallway passed into the most decadent of spaces. The living area was vast and the television so secondary and small. Staring at it David wondered if everything were from an arthouse catalogue. Now only the TV seemed familiar. Art Nouveau and deco all started to spin in his head like a movie spinning from end to beginning.

His brother sprang to mind, his brother wasn't here and his brother couldn't see what was happening now. So pretty, fast and spinning around and the TV was all that he could see now.

A scream so loud but it couldn't escape. Push, push, louder now. Why won't it escape. Nobody can hear me now.

Push, bite, screaming, cry nothing only darkness now.

Then a light, a horizontal white line then a blur of something not quite right.

Please please. They can't hear me. Relief at the grasping hands on him. Unspoken thanks hung in the air. But no smiles just a cloying stare. The grasping carried on as David's view cleared. Arnaud was here.

'Stop it, stop them,' as his clothes disappeared. Grasping, cloying muffled sounds. There was no way out. Arnaud stared through the flurry.

'Arnaud let me ooooooooooooout.'

The scream heaved David forward into a run for a door with digits and lights. Numbers he couldn't recall.

Sloping along the corridor he found another door.

A bed.

G.R.A.S.P.

Jacqui Cathcart

I look at myself in the mirror
and see that I've got thinner,
the grey bags under my eyes,
the clapped-in jaws I cannot disguise.

Depending on something is no fun,
especially if it is Heroin.
I think back to nearly two years ago,
I've probably changed more than I'll know.

I used to laugh and have lots of friends,
Go to the dancing at weekends.
I had boyfriends as well, well not a lot,
but at least I had them, now I've not.

I tell myself I really don't care,
but it would be nice if someone was there,
to hold me, to love me, to talk to me
and tell me I'm not just a hopeless Junkie.

Being a Junkie is one helluva habit,
I keep saying to myself 'I'm gonny get aff it,'
but I've been saying that for months,
and I've tried once or twice,
I wonder if I'll ever get back to being 'nice'.

A Junkie only has one friend,
your friend is the needle and that's where it ends.
All your real friends learned long ago,
it's a waste of time talking, you don't want to know.

You say you're not stupid,
You say you're not daft,
'I can stop if I want,
I only do it for a laugh.'

You laugh for a while,
and then start to cry,
when you realise you need
Junk to get by.

You lose your pride, your self respect too.
People start to talk about you.
You look a mess, but you don't care,
can't even be bothered to wash your hair.

You start to lose weight,
and your clothes don't fit,
but you don't buy some more
you'd rather have a Hit.

Then you start to lie and steal,
You beg for money, it ain't no big deal,
but somehow you manage each day
to get your smack, make the pain go away.

It's easy enough for people to say,
'Stop it now, start from today'
'Cos only a Junkie knows what it's like
to lie awake and sweat at night,
Cramps in your stomach, an aching back,
all because you've had no Smack.

Smack affects a lot of people,
not only the one who's hooked to the needle,
Most of all your Mum and Dad,

Where's the daughter they once had?
They beg and plead, try everything
to stop you using Heroin.
They can't understand, they don't see why
they have to watch you slowly die.

I started off laughing, now I'm in tears.
Is it really as long as nearly two years?
The worst two years of my life, no doubt.
I wish I had the strength to get out.

I try to think back to what I've done
before I started Heroin.
Had lots of fun and lots of friends
so why don't I try to do that again?

And as I sit here looking at me,
the face that looks back is a hopeless Junkie.
If only I had never heard the word Smack,
I wouldn't be here watching 'it' look back.

So, once again, I'm going to try
to stop relying on Junk to get by.
There must be more to life than drugs,
it's true what they say 'Drugs are for Mugs.'

So now it's time to start the battle,
to live each day without the needle,
it's going to be hard and will take a long time,
but, hopefully, this time success will be mine.

Shards

Christine Hewitt

The candle had drooped over to one side and spilled a pool of wax onto the bedside table. She remembered lighting it – one of those large church-style ones – as if that would keep her safe. She had lit it and picked up a drink. She had picked up the phone, to drink with him. She had got what she wanted, to get paralytic, but not like this. She hadn't signed up for this. This went way beyond feeling a fool. She heaved her head back into position and tried to keep as still as possible.

Now, there was a whole new realm of problems; dirty, repulsive problems. She needed to get up, get clean, clean everything, even her soul. A bath wouldn't wash that out. How could she even get to the bath? The floor was a sea of glass, the broken mirror glinted in the light of the television. On screen, two very together ladies silently sold stuff on the shopping channel. She thanked God for the mute function.

Come on. Soldier through, she heard her dad's voice say, as she always did at times like this. She thought of survival situations a soldier could suffer and the obstacles they could overcome but she couldn't even lift her head. And she had enough sense not to try. Her finger tips circled her scalp, locating lumps. There didn't seem to be a patch that wasn't raised or dented. Her brain tingled. At the top of her forehead she found something hard that felt like a zip. There was some sort of grit and when she pulled her hands away, she saw they were coiled in her own hair. It didn't seem to matter.

Her hands reached her throat. She wedged chunks of skin into her nails but there was no real sensation, her neck did not feel her own. It was as if her neck had retreated away inside. She too hid, clinging to the raft of her bed. She wasn't even clinging on for dear life. She simply clung.

Time passed over her. Dehydrated and surrounded by what, at a first glance, looked like sparkling treasure, she felt like she had awoken in a tomb. People weren't meant to wake up in tombs. She was convinced God was laughing at her. It was all a sick joke. If she could just get comfortable, achieve complete stillness and focus hard on believing her dreams to be real she could play dead, disappear from here, floating through into another dimension. A space where there was light and colour, softness and peace. She felt herself disperse into the air, into the air within the air, transcending into mere molecules. Even if the dream should turn bad it would still be better than this. She left it behind, never wanting to return.

A vision began to imprint itself on her mind: her body in the foetal position, encased in a liquid filled glass capsule, suspended from the ceiling of some steely laboratory, being pumped full of chemicals as part of some underground research project. She twitched her toes to see if she could feel them. She could. Clasping her knees she straightened her legs and felt something sharp prick her thigh, waking her.

Fuckin hell. There's even glass in my bed?

Even in this place it wasn't safe. The place where she would come back from the cusp of death. Her womb. How on earth was she supposed to go through the rebirthing process? It was absurd, she knew it. But she needed to believe in it. If the floor was anything to go by she could impale herself with the slightest flinch.

She lay there, still and pensive, running risk assessments in her head. Dare she gamble moving, bursting an artery and bleeding to death? She thought if she could imagine being the glass, she could become one with the glass, it would be less likely to attack her. It would be like attacking herself. That she could handle and for a moment, she felt safe.

Out on the street, she heard a door slam and a car accelerate off. It was loud. Was the front door open? She was sure she would have locked it but she couldn't be certain of anything anymore. What did it matter? An open door. Who could walk in and discover her? It occurred to her that everyone would turn on her. It was a definite eventuality. The evidence of her life had proved it to be inevitable. Everyone turned on her. It didn't matter who they were. It was the way of things, for her.

She was defective.

Just a piece of human scrap.

She should donate her organs.

I should just die.

There's no shame in going down with your own ship.

I should let this raft sink.

She knew she should do it soon before her body became useless, just as she was.

At least that would be something positive coming from all this. Being of some value in death as she knew she couldn't be in life. It was too late for her. Of that there was no doubt.

She winced. Her stomach was eating itself. It was almost a week since she had given it anything, she couldn't remember exactly. Her hip bone pointed at her in blame. Her exterior, her skin, lacked basic water. An additional coating of septic slime had grown. Her back and chest were layered in gloop, yet she couldn't have felt more naked. She pondered the possibility that her body had grown this putrid film as a protective layer, a chrysalis of contamination, cocooning her and ultimately saving her life.

Right then, the image of those black bottomless eyes engulfed her: staring right into her, with her staring right back. The air had cleared. She could see every detail. But she didn't want to see. The person sitting on her couch next to her was no longer her friend. Whoever this was didn't belong here. The lop-sided candle sizzled out. The two of them looked to see the black smoke stream upwards. He seemed to smile. Inside she started to crumble. He looked back at her as if eyeing her up for the first time. Who was this creature? His face had creased in a way she had never seen before. He straightened his back. Something else was in control. He moved slow and mechanical, one body part at a time. His head tilted to one side. His shoulders twisted towards her. What was he going to do to her? She had tried to get up but her seat seemed to disintegrate beneath her. Falling.

Between the bouts, she had tried to talk to him, tried to appeal to his better nature. She had tried everything but she had nothing in her defense. She was nothing more than its rag doll. She was nothing. Her life was in its hands and its hands were around her neck.

This wasn't ever going to stop. It was just going to keep coming for her over and over. She prayed, hard, trying to link herself to God in some way. God wasn't going to help her. She needed to do it herself.

The front door. She brought herself back to the here and now. If she was going to die it was going to be her way, and when she chose.

This was her territory. Hers. It was her body. And her rebirth could be from her, she just needed to be safe.

How to move? How to get up? She began strategizing the mechanics of how to get into some kind of vertical formation without the weight of her head snapping her neck. This would have to be executed carefully. There was no room for error. She was a puppet on its last string. Crossing her ankles, she held each side of her head and tucked her chin in. She took as deep a breath as she could, in anticipation of the pain. With a twist, she rolled over onto her back and let out a squawk as multiple other injuries made themselves known.

Her kidneys yelped. Her jaw felt like it was hanging off inside her face. The pain blanked her mind. Staring at the ceiling, through battery acid tears, she tried to find the strength to carry on. Gauging the distance to the edge of the bed, she wondered if the edge was too far or not far enough. She risked rolling and splatting face first onto the floor. *Just like an egg*. She laughed. Her mind was making fun of her and she was grateful for it.

She reached out a twig-like leg. Balancing herself, she hooked her knee onto the edge of the bed and leveraged up her body. She was careful to commando roll onto her forehead then slide her body down the side of the bed onto the floor and found herself kneeling in prayer. *This God is fuckin hilarious.*

As her knees took her weight, she felt the glass puncture her skin but she didn't care. She had made it, her spine intact. She un-cradled her neck, peeling off her hands to see if she could support her own head. She couldn't bear to touch where its hands had been for a moment longer. As long as she kept her head down and the top of her spine straight, she should be okay. It was crucial to keep the mobility she had left.

She had been in that bed so long she had felt part of it. Letting it go was a shock. Her body shook. She clutched her elbows to contain it. It was vital she didn't let her eyes wander onto the debris. What if she caught her reflection? She had enough to contend with. She would fix her eyes to only where they needed to be, where she was going to step.

Rising up onto her tip toes, she felt as if the glass was watching her. Her legs were bloodless, fizzling with pins and needles. Finding tiny gaps in the glass, she went one step at a time and slipped through the room as if trying not to awaken anything. On making it to the start of the corridor, she grabbed the door frame to steady her and peeped out through the bracken of her hair. The hall radiator was hanging off the wall. It didn't matter. All she needed to do was get to the other end, the end in darkness. She would go to the front door and check it was locked. Everything else could start from there. If she could just hold the front door handle in her hand and feel the bite that it was locked then she could, piece by piece, put herself back together again.

She made it past the relic of the radiator, her head flooding, remembering. She didn't want to know. She didn't want to think back but she couldn't stop. The mirror had exploded out of the wall. Like ice splicing the air. She saw herself fall in to her own image, shatter. The bang pierced the room, cloaking everything. Oblivion. No one moved. No one knew whose move it was or what the move should be. Had the black rage come to its end? Was this enough to bring back the friend she needed? Or was it a pause before the next onslaught? Time stuck. She hovered. She had felt sure the sound had been heard for miles but no one had come.

It was all on her.

Red. The door handle to the front door at the end of the corridor was red. Focus on the door. The corridor was the bridge to get there but the air felt hot in her lungs as she made her way along it and hot inside her neck. The salt in her sweat nipped at the wound on her forehead as she zeroed in on the little window near the door. From the window ledge, she dragged her body down the steps to the door and yanked on the handle.

THUNK.

She was safe. She should have trusted herself.

Whiteness.

She drooped forwards, head first and crouched with her face inches from the hard tile floor. Nobody would ever have to know about this. She felt feathers brush her and envelop her rib cage, slowing her flapping heart within. She breathed out a full breath, as her eyes closed.

When you open your eyes again, it will be your beginning.

Somewhere to Lay My Head

Robert Douglas

As I walk up Duke Street the Great Eastern Hotel looms ever higher – and nearer. It's a tall, rectangular block of a building. Five stories high, faced with grey concrete and rows of small, close-set windows. It looks like it belongs in the Bronx… or probably Skid Row.

I climb the wide steps up to the doors. A group of middle-aged men stand at the top, talking. I walk past them, straight into a musty, unlit lobby and approach 'Reception'. A man in a collar-less shirt, copper studs shining in the gloom, sits behind the counter, engrossed in the sports pages of the *Daily Record*. I'm surprised it's not *The New York Daily News*. I'll bet he's called Artie. Or Gus. He hasn't noticed me. There comes a noise from behind a half-open office door. I lean forward, expecting to see Edward G Robinson. My movement catches the eye of the Concierge. He looks up.

'Aye?'

Probably done his training at the Dorchester. 'Eh, how much is a room per week?'

He folds the paper.

'We don't dae rooms. It's cubicles. There's cubicles wi' windaes and cubicles withoot windaes. There's nae difference in room size. But the cubicles WI' windaes are thirty-five bob a week and the cubicles WITHOOT are thirty bob.'

I do a lightening calculation… Who needs a windae? I'd only be looking across the road at Duke Street Prison. It'll save me a pound a month.

'One withoot a windae, please.'

'Ah'll gie ye a look at it first. Some folk change their mind when they see them.'

Jeez! I wish he'd stop it, wi' that high-pressure salesmanship. He lifts a bunch of keys and I follow him into the lift. It's even shabbier than the lobby. There's a soupçon of last night's stale urine.

The lift door judders open at the third floor and we enter a dark, wood-panelled maze. There's a door every eight feet. After a series of turns he stops, inserts a key, then reaches a hand in to switch the light on.

Jeez-oh! I didn't know they made twenty watt light bulbs. I look at the cell-like room. There's a bed, small bedside table and a chair. No wardrobe, just hooks.

The Maître d'Dosshouse scratches his neck. 'Will this dae?'

'Aye, it'll be aw'right.'

He shows me the washroom. A row of twelve basins and six baths in cubicles. Then, in a non-stop monotone he runs through the house rules…

'Every Thursday moarning ye put oot wan pillowcase and wan sheet, also yer towel. Nae drunkenness allowed, nae noise that'll disturb yer fellow guests and the ootside door is locked at ten-thirty, prompt.'

He stops, draws a breath. Resumes…

'There's a canteen where ye can get cheap eats. If ye need a knock in the moarning, leave yer cubicle number at the desk and state whit time. We need a week in advance. If you've any other queries there's alwiz somebody oan at the desk.' He looks at me.

'Aye, that sounds fine.' I can't remember a word of it. But I'm bound to pick it up. 'I'll come doon tae the desk with ye and pay two weeks in advance.'

I return to the cubicle to take another look. It's even worse than it was the first time. The walls are made up of thin slats of wood, perhaps seven feet tall. There's no ceiling. The ACTUAL ceiling of the landing is about five feet higher. If somebody wants to get into a cubicle, it'll be easy to climb the slats and simply drop in. I sit on the bed, shrouded in the gloomy-twilight. Well, at least it's cheap. It's just somewhere to sleep. I look at Ma's wedding ring on my finger. Been there since December '54. I redeemed it from the Garscube Road pawnshop three days after she died. She'd been thirty-six. I was fifteen. My world had ended. So here we are three years later. I've graduated to the dosshouse.

I twist Ma's wedding ring round my finger. No matter HOW tough it gets, Ma, it won't be pawned again. I look at my watch. Four o'clock. Och, I'll away up to Maryhill. That'll cheer me up.

The number 23 trams run along Duke Street then on up to Maryhill. I'll wander round to Doncaster Street. It's always sad, but I still love being back in my old street. All my memories are there.

The tram glides to a halt at what we always called – 'oor stop'. I walk over to the pavement, turn, and as the tram pulls away it's like a curtain opening. Revealed, on the other side of the road, are scenes from my childhood. Some of the shops where Ma, with red Rexine shopping bag in one hand, the other holding mine, would visit on a daily basis to get – 'The Rations'. Nothing has changed…

Colman's Bakery, McGregor the fishmonger, Craig the butcher, Wilfred the hairdresser, the Post Office. I turn my head to the right. Ah! My two favourite memories – The Blythswood cinema and Cocozza's cafe. All through the war, and up until a fortnight before she died, we always considered these two as our 'Big Night' out. An evening at the pictures then, if she had enough money, an ice cream in Cocozza's. There was one other source of entertainment. The wireless. Ma and me loved it, and not just the music and comedy shows. By the time I was eight, I was a dedicated listener to radio plays. *Saturday Night Theatre* and, best of all, the horror stories presented by 'The Man in Black' – Valentine Dyall. Mr. Dyall, aided and abetted by the BBC sound effects department, used tae frighten the wits out of Ma and me every week without fail. We contributed to our own terror by always listening in the dark. And I'll tell you something else. Though you'll have to think about it. We got better pictures on the radio!

As I walk along Trossachs Street, I decide to pop into the wee shop. Say 'Hello' to Mr and Mrs Barlow…

'Hiyah!'

'Hello Robert! Haven't seen you for AGES.'

'I just came back to the city today. I've been missing it. Trouble is, I'll have to get myself a job as soon as possible, before the money runs oot.'

Mrs Barlow looks at me. Like many a Glasgow woman 'in business' she wears a hat when in the shop. That's the 'guinea's stamp' as Robert Burns would say. It shows that it's HER shop.

'Looking for a job are you?'

'Aye. The sooner the better.'

'I might be able to help you. I used to be secretary to the manager of the Clyde Navigation Trust. Would you like me to ring him and see if there are any vacancies?'

'Hey! That would be great.'

'Call in tomorrow afternoon, I'll have rang him by then. Mind! I'll be telling him you're a good lad. You won't let me down, will you?'

'I definitely won't.'

I leave the shop feeling immensely cheered up.

I turn the corner into Doncaster Street. Man! It just looks like always. When I was a kid I thought it was such a big street. Then I grew up, and suddenly it got small. I walk across the road towards my close in our tenement block; number fourteen. I want to stand again at the mouth of MY close. Lean against the wall and look up and down the street as if I still lived here.

Soon, I become lost in memories...

It's maybe twenty minutes later. From somewhere I suddenly know. Absolutely know. That a few yards behind me, where the close takes a dog-leg turn to the left – and our front door lies in the corner. Right at this moment, I'm aware it's painted brown again. Our large brass letterbox, with RJ Douglas on it, which my father took with him when he left. It's back on the door again. As long as I don't move from here, make no attempt to walk into the back close to take a look. It's all exactly as it was three years ago. But best of all. Right at this very minute I know my Ma's in the house, standing at the sink preparing veg for tonight's dinner. And for as long as I stay out here at the mouth of the close – she'll be just yards away, in the house. The linoleum will be wax-polished. The brasses shining bright. And as ever, a good fire will be burning in the range. Everything's as it would be in 1954. As long as I stay out here. In 1957.

It's getting late. I'm standing outside Cocozza's cafe, watching the trams glide up and down the Maryhill Road. They've got their lights on inside the saloons. I'll have to head off to the Great Eastern for my first night. I walk for a while, then eventually jump onto a No.23.

The lift door opens at the third floor. There are bulbs at the end of each stretch of narrow corridor. The bits inbetween are supposed to be lit by the overspill from the cubicles, after it's bounced off the dirty grey ceiling. Huh! Good luck with that. I open my door, switch on the light. I swear it's made the place darker! I look around. Dingy is the only word for it. The few pleasures of the day evaporate.

Cheer up! If you get that job with the Clyde Trust, you can get proper digs. You only sleep here.

I pick up the towel. It's so worn you could spit peas through it. I head for the washroom. If I had the choice – I think I'd rather SLEEP in the washroom. I already hate that word – 'cubicle'.

I'm in bed trying to read *The Colditz Story*. It's difficult to concentrate. The bed is hard. The bulb is so high up I have to lie at an angle to get enough light to read by. My fellow 'guests' are making some racket. They argue, talk loudly, shout across the open-tops of the cubicles.

Eventually, the adventures of the POWs help me to make my escape. I begin to doze… Oh, man! The light switch is up by the door. I climb out of bed, switch it off and get back into bed. I'm now wide awake. At 10.45 the night-watchman comes round, to knock on the doors of those showing lights. They all comply by switching off.

Conversations and arguments float over the partitions in the dark. Feeling low, I listen to their non-stop ramblings. What a place! Sooner I'm out of here the better. I hope Ma doesn't know where I am. 'It's just temporary, Ma. Honest.'

I get the job with the Clyde Navigation Trust!

Soon, I'm into a routine. Every morning, Monday to Friday, the night-watchman gives me my early knock. I'm up like a linty and into the washroom. As it's 6am I have the place to myself. As I exit and head back to my cubicle, the fetid smell of the sleeping area hits me. I never notice it when I wake up. Probably get used to it overnight. Jeez! It's really strong. Reminiscent of the smell of a tram driver's jockstrap.

I love my Glasgow mornings. No matter what dock I'm working at, in whatever district of the city, I know I'll soon come across a wee dairy, followed by a newsagent. They are mandatory every three streets. As I open the door of the dairy, a brass bell jangles above my head. They all sound the same. Somewhere, there must be a company called 'The Acme Dairy Door Bell Company, Ltd'. I'm immediately surrounded by the smell of fresh-baked rolls and cold cuts of meat. I buy four well-done rolls and either slices of tongue, ham or corned beef. Plus a little pat of butter. I check that my shiny brass tea and sugar tin is full.

Arriving at the site early, I let the night-watchman go off. I now have the bothy to myself for an hour. I prepare my four rolls then brew a large mug of tea. Warmed by the hut's cast iron stove, I eat two of the rolls for breakfast as I read my paper. The other two are kept for mid-day.

After I finish work and head off for the Great Eastern, I soon have a number of cafes, or fish and chip shops, where I can get some dinner.

I love working on the river. In 1957 – years before containerisation – cargo boats and tramp steamers from all over the world sail into the Clyde and tie up in various docks. Soon, dockers are swarming all over them, uncovering their holds while dockside cranes glide alongside. It isn't long before nets full of cargo are being lifted out of their holds and swung down to the quayside.

Meanwhile, mostly on the south shore of the river, ships are under construction in various yards. The sounds of riveting and the flicker of welder's torches play a Glasgow gavotte, all day long. I like being even a small part of it.

I'm in a gang of fifteen guys who are responsible for maintaining the docks, wharves and sheds. We take our bothy, which is easy to disassemble, to all the docks where we are sent to work. The River Clyde is a hive of industry in the 1950s. The lads I work with are typical Glasgow fellas. We all get on well, and the banter is great. Glasgow guys have a simple philosophy…

'If you HAVE to go to work, you might as well make the best of it. Have a laugh!' It really works.

Now I'm earning, I should be looking for digs. But I've got so used to the Great Eastern, it doesn't bother me like when I first arrived. It's just where I sleep. There is one bonus now that I'm working. I don't do my own laundry anymore. I take it to a nearby laundry. I go out every night. Sometimes with my boyhood pal, Sammy Johnston. Or I go to the pictures. In between times, I visit Sammy's house a few evenings. We usually play cards for coppers. His Ma and Da, Frank and Lottie, always make me welcome.

Suddenly, it's the end of September. I've been here for three months. Right! I'm gonna make the effort. One more month and that is IT! I'll look for lodgings.

The only resident I'll miss when I leave is Dieter. I often sit with him and have a blether. A former German soldier, he was taken prisoner in France after D-Day. He's probably about forty years old.

With a German helmet on, he would fit everyone's idea of a typical Kraut. In reality, he's a kind-hearted soul. Since I got to know him, I've come to the conclusion that Dieter would be a happy guy if he had a nice lady friend. Sadly, what with his unprepossessing looks, I would imagine that the last time Dieter pulled – it was the pin out of a grenade!

We are sitting together in the canteen. The Concierge approaches. 'There's somebody oot in the foyer asking fur you.' The foyer? Oh! He must mean the loaby!

'For me?'

'Aye. Robert Douglas.'

It's my pal, Sammy.

'This is a surprise. What's the matter?'

'Whit it is, I've gone and let slip that you're living here. Ah wiz talking tae my Ma, and I forgot I'm no' supposed tae tell anybody.'

'Och! That's OK. You didn't have tae bother coming doon…' He interrupts me.

'Aye, but the trouble is. When she heard where ye were living she played hell wi' me for no' telling her. She's sent me doon tae tell ye, you've tae pack up and leave this minute. You can come and stay wi' us until ye get yersel real digs. I've not tae come back withoot ye!'

Forty minutes later I watch Sammy open his door. I prepare myself for, 'The Wrath of Lotisha'…

'Whit urr you daeing living in that dump and no' letting oan tae anybody?'

'Sammy knew.'

'He's as daft as you, so that's nae buggering help! Right. Ye can stay here until ye get yerself digs.' She takes a draw on an ever-present Woodbine, 'OR, until ye get oan ma tits and Ah throw ye oot! Anywye, urr ye hungry?'

'Ah wiz eating mince and tatties. But they were awfy greasy.'

'Will ye manage bacon and eggs?'

'Oh, aye. That wid be lovely.'

Her husband, Frank, has been sitting listening. Frank is one of the kindest, gentlest men I've ever known. A petty officer sick-berth attendant on an 'escort' aircraft carrier – HMS Vindex – he spent three dangerous years on Russian convoys during the war. Nowadays he's a male nurse at Ruchill Hospital.

'Frank! Put the kettle oan and get the frying pan oot.'

He sighs, looks at me. 'Ah'm just in fae ma work.' He turns to his beloved. 'Can Ah no' huv a minute tae maself?'

'Yer arse in parsley!' says Lottie, from behind a low bank of Cumulus Woodbinus.

So ended my short experience of residing in a 'MINUS star' hotel. Since then I've booked into various Hiltons, Malmaisons and other upmarket hotels. Even had tea at the Ritz. I feel certain that those months spent in the Great Eastern, now sixty years ago, helped me to appreciate the good times – when they eventually arrived.

Brendan

Gillean McDougall

He only opens the door a couple of inches.

'Look, you know it's me, I told you I was coming.'

'Yes. Yes.'

'So open the door.'

The stink of rotten food hits me, and I have to push the door really hard to get it to give. The hall is full of black bin bags. Some are falling open, food overflowing on the floor.

'Brendan, these bags were here the last time I came to see you.'

'I know. Don't do this, you said you wouldn't do this.'

'I have to check on you so I can tell mum, you know that. We need to know you're OK.'

'I'm OK. This is OK. Don't worry.'

I look round the hall. All the doors to the rooms are closed, and I dread opening them. 'Shall we go out for a coffee?'

He's found a woman's coat from somewhere, a great long black thing, silky, frayed at the edges. It nearly reaches his ankles and I want to laugh.

It's not summer yet, there's only a watery sun. People are walking their dogs on the esplanade. Older couples are out having a stroll, either on holiday or maybe living in this wee sleepy town. The wind comes off the sea in gusts. They smile at us, thinking we're normal, although the coat's a bit of a giveaway. It's a strong wind but the smell of the flat is still with me. I can feel it hanging in my clothes.

There's an illuminated display in the cafe; livid colour photographs of food. When it's shovelled on the plates it looks different. Brendan spends ages gazing at one wall, then turns his whole body round to look at another. The old Italian guy is looking at me with a tired face.

'I'll just have a coffee, thanks, black coffee.'

'Wan Americano, comin up. An the boy?'

He's still staring at the photos.

'Brendan?'

He ignores me, turns abruptly on his heel and heads for the table at the window. I decide for him.

'The all-day breakfast, thanks, just for one.'

'You wan hash brown or chips, tea or coffee?'

I don't know what he wants. What did he have the last time? 'Chips, tea, thanks.'

'Siddown, I bring ya.'

'Thanks.' I pay and take my coffee. Brendan's drumming on the edge of the table with his fingers and scanning the view anxiously. Drops of rain start streaking down the windows.

'Do you come here through the week?'

'No, no.' He's waving his head back and forth like windscreen wipers. 'Well, sometimes. No.'

The coffee is feeble but hot. It's in a luminescent cup, translucent white like church alabaster. 'So? You grew a beard?'

He laughs. I haven't seen him laugh in such a long time. When he laughs he looks the way he used to. He strokes his new beard. It suits him. I lean across and pick at a crumb in it with my nail. The hair is softer than I expect. My little bearded brother.

'You look nice. Makes you look handsome.'

He laughs again, and I remember the time before it all went wrong. Mum had said, he'll kill himself, sleeping rough.

'And the flat, that working out OK?'

'Yes, yes.' His fingers start drumming again.

'You should try to get the rubbish down to the bin. Did the social worker not say you should do that?'

'Yes, I do. I do do that. Yes, I do.'

There's a clatter as the Italian guy puts Brendan's plate down with a flourish. 'And the signorina, no food today? You no wan a wee pie?'

He's being quite nice this time. 'No, but thanks anyway.'

'Hey, Brendan, you enjoy yer food, OK?' He shuffles away as Brendan dives into the plate, holding his knife and fork in his fists like a child. There's a line of old grazes across the knuckles of one hand.

I watch the old man lifting the flap of the counter, turning, replacing it. He must have done it thousands of times.

'He knows your name.' Brendan's munching so hard he's not

paying me any attention. He must be starving. I listen to the sound of his chewing and swallowing and stir my coffee. I put the hot alabaster to my lips occasionally and watch the people outside, fighting with umbrellas now against the wind.

When he's finished the food he turns to the tea, pouring and stirring with great concentration. It'll take hours for him to finish at this rate. I go to the toilet. Better going here than back at the flat. A sign is taped to the wall beside the basin – 'Family Fun Day'. There's a photograph of a clown and children with balloons and ice creams.

I spend more time than I need to drying my hands on thin paper towels that disintegrate between my fingers. When I come out, Brendan's gone. His empty plate is sitting alongside a full cup of tea and he's disappeared. Nobody saw him go. They look at me as if I'm the daft one.

Out on the esplanade I expect to see him and the black coat fluttering behind him. Nowhere. I cross the road and look down to the beach, acres of wet sand stretching in both directions. It's stopped raining, more people are walking, but he's not here. He's just gone. My heart's pounding. I take in deep breaths, let them out slowly through my lips, concentrating on the sensation, trying not to panic.

I write my phone number on a paper napkin and give it to the man in the cafe. He shrugs, he doesn't care. 'He come back, we phone, sure. Don worry.'

He's not at the flat either. I think I'll give him an hour and start clearing up. I risk opening the doors to the living room, bedroom and bathroom. Every room looks the same; dirty, not lived in. His bed isn't made up – a new pack of sheets is on the floor. He's sleeping in a sleeping bag on top of the mattress.

I fill five black bags and take them to the bins, then scrub the sticky floor. The washing machine looks as if it's never been used; I wash all the clothes I can find, not looking at them too closely. After a couple of hours, I phone the social worker.

She sounds pissed off with me. 'Well, he does this sometimes, it's nothing to worry about. I'm due to see him Tuesday. Sometimes he doesn't turn up. It's nothing to worry about.'

'So you're saying that nothing will have happened to him? What if something does?'

'Your brother's nearly forty. You have to let him live his own life.' The atmosphere on the line bristles with her irritation.

I scrape congealed food off plates, boil kettles to fill the basin with hot water, soak pans that have been used over and over again without being washed. I put the food I've bought in the empty fridge, clear a space to walk in through the flat. I find his armchair, plump the cushions.

In the hall, I notice that someone has hung a long thin paper calendar on the wall. Each month has a picture of a kitten at the top. There's nothing written in it except 'Linda' at the same time every Tuesday.

It's dark by the time I leave, and starting to rain again. I don't have an umbrella. The cafe is closing, a young boy pulling down the shutters with a clatter. The trains are every hour on a Sunday and I've just missed one.

Between the cafe and the station, there's a pub. The sign says 'The Good Prospect' and the windows are low, as if it's been there for centuries and has sunk into the ground with old age. Through the small glass panes it looks deserted, but the lights are cheery and I'm freezing.

The barman pours me a double brandy, takes my money and gives me change without saying a word. I sit down in an uncomfortable chair because it's beside a fire. I'll lie to mum, won't tell her he shot off like that. He's not dead, I cleaned up, at least I saw him. The brandy burns a warm trail down my throat.

'You a day tripper? Bus go without you?' The man at the next table is smiling at me. Nice guy, blond, older. He has a green wax jacket that looks crisp and new, and where he's holding his pint glass his fingers are plump and round. I take another mouthful of brandy and the heat of it propels my mind into fast-forward. I imagine us kissing, fucking. Maybe this place has rooms upstairs. I want to be in a warm, clean bed that belongs to no one. I want to be asleep.

I smile back, no harm. 'I've been visiting my brother.'

He's turning to face me, his hand reaching out for his wallet on the table. I watch his lips opening and out of the corner of my eye something passes the low window behind him. It's Brendan, shoulders hunched, black coat trailing behind him. As I whip through the swing doors I catch the barman's smile. 'Bye then.' So he can speak after all.

On the pavement, I put my arm through his. He doesn't look surprised. 'I'll walk you home then I have to get my train.'

'OK. Just walk me to the corner. And wave to me. Three times.'

'Yes, I know.' We always wave three times.

As we get to the station, I dig in my bag for the envelope with the money in it, passed from mum to me and now to him. He doesn't say anything, just crushes the buff paper in his fingers. I hug him and think how thin he is under that stupid black coat, his body tense against mine like always.

The concourse is bright with fluorescent strip lights, and as I'm buying my ticket I can see the train waiting across the shiny white tiles, people rushing to get on. The machine makes comforting noises and out fall my ticket and a silver stream of loose change.

Across the road, Brendan's on the street corner, looking at me, not moving. As I see him, his white hand strafes the darkness like a bird, three times. Then he turns and heads for home.

Getting Involved in Volunteering

Jacqui Cathcart

When I came to the NW I was quite shy
But as the days and weeks and months went by
My self esteem and my confidence grew
As I listened to what it is we do.

I started off helping when I could
Being part of NW felt so good
I knew it was special, it was so great
Something to get involved in to keep me straight.

There's Women's & Men's groups, a drop-in too
Loads in the community for folk to do
With people in Recovery showing the way
Delivering these groups every day.

I started off being part of the Team
Now I'm delivering the groups I've seen
NW is a force that's so very good
For everyone in the neighborhood.

We're showing that there is a way out
Of addiction, that's what we are all about
Helping the community to heal with us
Being a volunteer is such a buzz.

We're trying to put a little bit back
In our community that was wrecked with smack
We're getting there we really are
Can't believe we've come so far.

Breaking down barriers that are there
Showing we're people who really care
Building relationships along the way too
That is what we are trying to do.

Volunteers and Staff side by side
Working in partnership there's no divide
Promoting recovery in every way
in our communities day by day.

Recovery Communities are happening today
Such a great achievement wouldn't you say
Volunteers are getting repaid too
With lots of training opportunities we can do.

From Gender-Based Violence, Child Protection too
Setting up a Recovery Community near you
Writing a report, negotiating skills
Making funding applications and paying bills.

These are just a few but there's so much
So if you want to volunteer then get in touch
The future's exciting it's all so great
I love being a Volunteer and being straight.

A Message From Glasgow Libraries

We all take enormous pride as Glaswegians that our city is a welcoming, supportive and friendly place for residents and visitors alike. As Glaswegians its part of our DNA to do our bit to help and support others and to do what we can for those that need the help we can offer. We're all individuals with hopes, dreams and aspirations and through stories and books we can often find common ground. We hope this book will inspire us all to do more and to support our fellow 'Weegies'.

Our libraries are located right across the city and every day they offer a safe and welcoming space for all. We offer people information, advice and support to help with their needs. We're part of a strong network of community based services that sustain the people of Glasgow. We want to take this opportunity to share information about key provisions for people affected by homelessness. If we all know more about where to seek support when it's needed then we'll all be able to do that bit more for others. After all, its people – who we are, what we know, and what we do – that make Glasgow.

The Glasgow Homelessness Network is a third sector membership organisation with a unique role to support advancing solutions to poor housing and homelessness by connecting the knowledge and experiences of people who both live and work with the issue. The Network connects with organisations from all over the city to support people affected by homelessness. Further information can be found on their web site and they can offer support and connection for individuals to services that can help them with their needs: www.ghn.org.uk/hip/

Thank You

Thank you to the contributing writers in this book. We met you because Glasgow hosted the Homeless World Cup, but that wasn't the end of our relationship. We have enjoyed working with you all through your creative writing experiences and this book is testament to your stories, experiences, imagination and creativity. You've inspired us with your passion and determination and your stories, poetry and prose have had a profound effect on us. Your writing truly is inspirational and moving. We look forward to continuing to support you with your writing, learning and wherever your personal journey takes you next.

Thanks go to programme providers and individuals who helped us create this book by sharing their knowledge and talent.